# Penguin Grammar Workbook 1 Beginners

## Peter Dainty

**Series Editor: Edward Woods**

## CONTENTS

PENGUIN BOOKS

Published by the Penguin Group
Penguin Books Ltd, 27 Wrights Lane, London W8 5TZ, England
Penguin Putnam Inc., 375 Hudson Street, New York, New York 10014, USA
Penguin Books Australia Ltd, Ringwood, Victoria, Australia
Penguin Books Canada Ltd, 10 Alcorn Avenue, Toronto, Ontario, Canada M4V 3B2
Penguin Books (NZ) Ltd, 182–190 Wairau Road, Auckland 10, New Zealand

Penguin Books Ltd, Registered Offices: Harmondsworth, MIddlesex, England

Published by Penguin Books 1998
10 9 8 7 6 5 4 3 2

Illustration on page 55 by Chris Chaisty, and illustrations on
page 78 by Bob Harvey, Pennant Ilustrations

Set in Times and Helvetica
Printed and bound by Bath Press Colourbooks, Glasgow

# Introduction

*Penguin Grammar Workbook 1* is for beginners who need practice in those elementary grammar structures which are necessary for basic communication, and on which other grammatical structures can be built. The students are not yet preparing for exams.

## WHY IS GRAMMAR IMPORTANT?

Many people think that grammar is not important because people can understand them even when they make mistakes. People can understand simple information when you are telling them what you are doing or where you've been, even if you do make mistakes. However, when you make mistakes, the other person will soon get tired of listening to you.

## PENGUIN GRAMMAR WORKBOOK 1

The aim of the *Workbook* is to provide you with a lot of practice work to improve your use of grammar.

The 41 units in the book cover all the important basic grammatical structures to help you use English well. In addition to practising the way a structure is formed, there is also practice with how it is used.

While most units cover two pages, there are some which are only one page in length. These are for structures that do not need a lot of practice.

## A typical unit

**1 Explanation box** Here you will find examples of the structure and short explanations of how it is formed and when it is used. In some cases, where the unit is comparing the use of two different structures, e.g. the present simple and the present continuous (Unit 10), we focus on the different uses of the two structures, showing how they are used to mean different things.

**2 Practice Exercise** Most of the units have five or six exercises. The first three are for you to practice the form and the last two are to practice the use. There are often dialogues, short stories or are task based.

Where there is a lot of information, e.g. Adjectives 1: Positive and *as ... as* (Unit 32), this is divided into two parts – some at the beginning and the rest after Exercise 3. In these cases, Exercises 1, 2, and 3 practise what is in the first box. Exercises 4 and 5 practise what is in the second box.

## Testing your Grammar

At stages throughout the book, there is a Revision Test. There are four Revision Tests – after Units 10, 23, 31 and 41. There are thirty-five to forty items in each test. These are arranged in small groups so that you can quickly see what kinds of mistakes you are making and where you can find the information to help you and get more practice.

At the end of the book there is an Exit Test. When you have done the Exit Test, you will see if you are ready to go on to *Workbook 2*.

## The Answer Key

In the centre of the book, you will find the Answer Key for all the exercises and tests in the book. You can take this out of the book if you wish.

## The End of the Book

At the end of the book, there are four sections to help you.

**1 Glossary:** this section explains the meanings of some grammar terms.

**2 Irregular verbs:** this is a list of the most common irregular verbs, giving the infinitive, the simple past and the past participle.

**3 Punctuation:** this gives you information on when to use capital letters, commas, and full stops.

**4 Spelling:** this is information to help you with plural and comparative forms.

## FOR THE STUDENT

You can use this book to work on your own to improve your use of grammar. If you want to, you can work through the book from the beginning. We expect many of you, however, will want to spend more time practicising the structures you find difficult. Different people have different problems. Look at the Contents page at the beginning of the book. This will tell you where you can find the grammatical structures you are looking for.

Always read the explanation box carefully before doing the practice exercises. It is not necessary to do every exercise at once. At first, you should do only one or two. Go back and do the other exercises at a later date. This will give you extra practice when you feel you need it.

Some of the exercises are in the form of dialogues. On these occasions you can practise speaking the dialogue with a friend.

## FOR THE TEACHER

You can use this book as a grammar course book or as a supplementary book to give your students extra practice when they need it. It will also be useful for homework tasks.

In the classroom, the exercises which are in the form of dialogues (e.g. Unit 9, Exercise 5) can be used for role-play and pair work. There are also exercises which can be used as group work tasks.

# UNIT 1 Present Tense of *to be* 1: Positive and Negative

I am cold; He is French; They are rich

## FORM

**Look at these sentences.**

*I **am** a teacher.*      *(I'm a teacher.)*
*She **is** French.*      *(She's French.)*
*It **is** cold.*      *(It's cold.)*
*They **are** rich.*      *(They're rich.)*

The verb *to be* has three forms in the present tense –
*am*, *is* and *are*.

**POSITIVE**

| **Long form** | **Short form** |
|---|---|
| I am | I'm |
| You are | You're |
| He / She / It is | He's / She's / It's |
| We / You / They are | We're / You're / They're |

*I'm hungry.*
*Pam **is** at school.*
*They **are** blue and red.*

**NEGATIVE**

| **Long form** | **Short form** |
|---|---|
| I am not | I'm not |
| You are not | You aren't |
| He / She / It is not | He / She / It isn't |
| We / You / They are not | We / You / They aren't |

*I'm not hungry.*
*Lisbon **isn't** in Spain.*
*We **are not** rich.*

**Note:**
We normally use the short form *(I'm, I'm not)* in
conversation.

## USE

**1** We use *am*, *is* and *are*
**A** to say what we do
*I'm a doctor.*
*She's a dentist.*
**B** to say where we live
*I'm from Paris.*
*They're from Argentina.*
**C** to talk about nationality
*I'm Turkish.*
*They're French.*
**D** to describe things or people
*I'm tired.*
*You're beautiful.*
*The bus **is** yellow.*

These questions **are** difficult.
**E** to say where things are
*Lisbon **is** in Portugal.*
*Tokyo and Kyoto **are** in Japan.*
**2** We also use *it is* (*it's*)
**A** to talk about the weather
*It's hot today.*
*It's very cold in here.*
**B** for time
*It's half past ten.*
*It's one o'clock.*

## 1 Write the short form

*Write the short form of the positive.*
**Example:**
I am *I'm*

1   we are ..............
2   he is ..............
3   they are ..............
4   she is ..............
5   you are ..............

## 2 Write the short form

*Write the short form of the negative.*
**Example:**
I am not *I'm not*

1   we are not ..............
2   he is not ..............
3   they are not ..............
4   she is not ..............
5   you are not ..............

## 3 Complete the sentences

*Complete the sentences. Use long forms of the positive* (am, is, are).
**Example:**
The weather *is* beautiful. Let's go to the beach.

1 My brother .......... a doctor.
2 I .......... hungry. Let's have dinner.
3 The cinema .......... near the station.
4 Fred and Jane .......... in the park.
5 This tea .......... cold.
6 The door .......... open.
7 Her house .......... very small.
8 I .......... French. My husband .......... Spanish. My boss .......... Chinese.
9 The bananas .......... green. Don't eat them!
10 The floor .......... wet. Be careful!
11 He .......... very tired.
12 They .......... thirsty. Give them some tea.
13 We .......... late again.
14 I .......... sorry.
15 It .......... a beautiful day, and I .......... very happy.

## 4 Complete the sentences

*Complete the sentences. Use short forms of the positive* ('m, 's, 're).
**Example:**
We*'re* happy.

1 I .......... thirsty.
2 He .......... rich.
3 It .......... eight o'clock.
4 It .......... very cold today.
5 We .......... ready.
6 She .......... in the bathroom.
7 I .......... very tired.
8 The taxi .......... here. Let's go.
9 You .......... right. I .......... wrong.
   I .......... sorry.
10 We .......... in a hurry. Be quick!
11 The window .......... open.
12 Pierre .......... French, but his wife .......... German.
13 They .......... on holiday at the moment.
14 We .......... hungry.
15 Good, dinner .......... ready.

## 5 Complete the sentences

*Complete the sentences. Use long forms of the negative* (am not, is not, are not). *The first one has been done for you.*

1 I *am not* rich! I am poor.
2 She .......... here today. She is on holiday.
3 Tokyo .......... in Singapore. It is in Japan.
4 My brother .......... a teacher. He is a doctor.
5 The bus .......... blue. It is yellow.
6 You .......... right! You are wrong!
7 This bread .......... fresh. Don't eat it.
8 Jim and Vivienne .......... Australian. They are American.
9 My jumper .......... red. It is blue.
10 It .......... 2 o'clock. It's 3 o'clock. Let's go!
11 The film .......... good. It is bad.
12 Caviare .......... cheap. It is very expensive.
13 We .......... happy. We are very angry.
14 My car .......... big. It is small.
15 I .......... a student. I am a teacher.

## 6 Complete the sentences

*Complete the sentences. Use short forms of the negative* ('m not, isn't, aren't).
**Example:**
Indonesia *isn't* in Europe. It's in Asia.

1 I' .......... French. I'm Italian.
2 She .......... Italian. She's French.
3 The river .......... very clean. Don't swim in it.
4 My brothers .......... here. They're in Australia.
5 These questions .......... easy. I need some help.
6 The film .......... interesting. Let's go home.
7 An orange .......... a vegetable. It's a fruit.
8 A carrot .......... a fruit. It's a vegetable.
9 My bicycle .......... blue. It's yellow.
10 Betty .......... here today. She's on holiday.
11 It .......... warm today. It's cold.
12 We .......... hungry now. Let's eat later.
13 John .......... my father. He's my grandfather.
14 I .......... ready. Please wait.
15 This food .......... bad. It's perfect.

## Present Tense of *to be* 2: Questions
### Am I early? Is it cold? Are they ready?

## FORM

**1** Look at these sentences.
*Am I early?*
*Are you ready?*
*Is he Portuguese?*
*Is the soup hot?*
*Are they cold?*
These are question forms of the verb *to be*.
**2** To make a question, we put *am*, *is* or *are* at the beginning of the sentence.
Am I right?
Is he / she / it right?
Are we / you / they right?

**3** We often give a short answer to a question with *am*, *is* or *are*.
*Are you* happy?       *Yes, I am. / No, I'm not.*
*Is it* cold in here?    *Yes, it is. / No, it isn't.*

**SHORT ANSWERS**

| Positive | Negative |
|---|---|
| Yes, I am | No, I'm not |
| Yes, he / she / it is | No, he / she / it isn't |
| Yes, we / you / they are | No, we / you / they aren't |

## USE

**1** We use *am*, *is* and *are* to ask
**A** what people do
*Is she a doctor?*
**B** where people live
*Are you from Argentina?*
**C** about people's nationality
*Is she Chinese?*
**D** how people feel
*Are you ill?*
**E** what things and people are like

*Is the bus yellow?*
*Is the man tall?*
**F** where things are
*Is Lisbon in Portugal?*
*Is the book on the table?*
**2** We also use *is it* to ask about
**A** the weather
*Is it hot today?*
**B** the time
*Is it one o'clock?*

---

### 1  Make questions

*Make questions. Add am, is or are.*
**Example:**
*Is* Fred here?

**1** .......... you happy?
**2** .......... it difficult to speak Chinese?
**3** .......... she good at tennis?
**4** ......... dinner ready?
**5** ......... these computers expensive?
**6** ......... your hands clean?
**7** ......... your flat cold in the winter?
**8** ......... I wrong?
**9** ......... the window open?
**10** .......... the people in your office friendly?
**11** .......... he French?
**12** .......... the dogs good with children?
**13** .......... I late again?
**14** .......... it easy to find a good house here?
**15** .......... we ready to go?

### 2  Make questions

*Put the words in the right order to make questions.*
**Example:**
rich / are / you  *Are you rich?*

**1** ready / are / you
.................................................?
**2** well / are / you
.................................................?
**3** is / big / your garden
.................................................?
**4** these shoes / expensive / are
.................................................?
**5** this answer / is / right
.................................................?
**6** thirsty / you / are
.................................................?
**7** your neighbours / friendly / are
.................................................?
**8** the airport / open / is
.................................................?

**9** this / important / is

.......................................?

**10** are / fresh / these vegetables

.......................................?

**11** coffee / hot / that / is

.......................................?

**12** early / I / am

.......................................?

**13** now / rich / are / we

.......................................?

**14** me / angry with / he / is

.......................................?

**15** American / car/ your / is

.......................................?

## 3  Make questions

*Make questions. Put the underlined words in the right order.*

**Example:**

It is very cold in here. open / the window / is ?

It is very cold in here. *Is the window open?*

**1** This song is beautiful. is / Spanish / it ?
**2** I think New York is the capital of America. right / am / I ?
**3** That jumper is beautiful. Italian / it / is ?
**4** What's the time? 9 or 10 / is / it ?
**5** Fred is a doctor. rich / is / he ?
**6** Jackie's in the kitchen. hungry / is / she ?
**7** There are some sandwiches on the table. are / fresh / they ?
**8** He thinks English grammar is easy. is / wrong / he ?
**9** I'm ready. taxi here / the / is ?
**10** Where's the dog? in the garden / it / is ?
**11** We're late for the cinema. ready / you / are ?
**12** That painting is beautiful. it / expensive / is ?
**13** This car's very old. it / in / are / safe / we ?
**14** Where is Mauritius? is / in the Indian Ocean / it ?
**15** I like your friend. Japanese / she / is ?

## 4  Make questions and give short answers

**Examples:**

*Is* she hungry?          Yes, she *is*
*Are* they Indian?          No, they *aren't*.

**1** .......... your feet cold?          Yes, they ..........
**2** .......... breakfast ready?          No, it ..........
**3** .......... the water hot?          No, it ..........

**4** .......... your sister well?          Yes, she ..........
**5** .......... the buses in London red?          Yes, they ..........
**6** .......... the taxis in New York yellow?          Yes, they ..........
**7** .......... the bank open?          No, it ..........
**8** .......... your hotel expensive?          No, it ..........
**9** .......... her eyes blue?          Yes, they ..........
**10** .......... this bread fresh?          No, it ..........
**11** .......... he your husband?          Yes, he ..........
**12** .......... you tired?          No, I ..........
**13** .......... they here?          No, they ..........
**14** .......... your coffee nice?          Yes, it ..........
**15** .......... we late?          No, we ..........

## 5  Match the questions

*Write* am, is *or* are *to make questions in A. Then match the questions to the answers in B. The first one has been done for you.*

**A**

**1** *Is* Jenny in the office?
**2** .......... I in the photograph?
**3** .......... the newspaper in the kitchen?
**4** .......... Hungary in Asia?
**5** .......... it difficult to understand golf?
**6** .......... your father a doctor?
**7** .......... these cookery books interesting?
**8** .......... this milk fresh?
**9** .......... we near the sea
**10** .......... your car new?
**11** .......... your shoes clean?

**B**

a) No, it's twenty years old!
b) Yes, I love reading books.
c) No, it's in Europe.
d) No, it's in the bathroom.
e) Yes, I bought it yesterday.
f) Yes, you can go for a swim if you like.
g) No, she's at home today.
h) Yes, there you are. You're standing near my sister.
i) No, they are dirty.
j) No, it's an easy game.
k) No, he's a dentist.

# UNIT 3 Present Tense of *to have*
## She has beautiful eyes

## FORM

Look at these sentences.
*She **has** brown hair.*
*Fred **has** three children.*
*I **have** toothache – is there a good dentist near here?*
*We **have** a new teacher. She's wonderful!*
*Has* and *have* are the present simple forms of the verb *to have*.

**POSITIVE**
Subject + *has* / *have*

| I / You / We / They | have |
| He / She / It | has |

*We **have** a new Porsche.*
*Daniel **has** black hair and blue eyes.*

**NEGATIVE**
Subject + *do not* / *does not* + *have*

**Long form:**

| I / You / We/ They | do not | have |
| He / She / It | does not | have |

**Short form:**

| I/ You / We / they | don't | have |
| He / She / It | doesn't | have |

*Jim and his wife **don't have** children.*
*That school **doesn't have** a computer.*
**Note:**
We normally use the short form in conversation.

**QUESTIONS**
*do* / *does* + subject + *have*?

| Do I / you / we / they | have? |
| Does he / she / it | have? |

***Do** you **have** a car?*
***Does** Janet **have** a brother?*

## USE

**1** We use *has* and *have* to talk about
**A** things we do regularly
*I **have** lunch at the office.*
*She **has** three cups of tea a day.*
*Jackie always **has** a shower before breakfast.*
**B** our families and people we know
*I **have** one brother and three sisters.*
*She **has** two sons, three daughters and 15 grandchildren.*
*I **have** a penfriend in South Africa. She writes to me every month.*
**C** how we look and how we feel
*She **has** beautiful eyes.*
*He **has** very small feet.*
*I **have** a headache – I'm going to bed.*

**D** things we possess
*I **have** a car.*
*He **has** three houses.*
*They **have** a lot of money.*
**Note:**
In British English we often use *has got* and *have got* to say the ideas in B, C and D. (*See* Unit 4)
*I **have got** one brother.*
***She's got** beautiful eyes.*
***They've got** a lot of money.*
**2** We sometimes put the word *any* after *don't have* / *doesn't have* to make the sentence stronger.
*I can't buy you a dog. I don't have **any** money.*
*James can't come to the party. He doesn't have **any** time.*

---

### 1 Complete the sentences

*Complete the sentences with* has *or* have.
**Example:**
I *have* five sisters.

1  He .......... a bath every day.
2  They .......... dinner at about 8.30.
3  My dog .......... green eyes.
4  She .......... a good job.
5  He .......... brown hair.

6  Mr and Mrs Simpson .......... five children.
7  I .......... two holidays a year.
8  We .......... a new car.
9  He always .......... three slices of toast for breakfast.
10  I .......... a headache. This music is very loud!
11  We .......... two dogs.
12  They .......... a house by the sea.
13  She .......... a French husband.
14  I .......... two brothers and one sister
15  He .......... friends all over the world.

## 2 Make the sentence negative

*Make the sentences negative. Use* don't have *or* doesn't have.

**Example:**
I have a bicycle.
*I don't have a bicycle.*

1  They have a cat.                    ....................
2  She has red hair.                   ....................
3  She has an expensive watch.         ....................
4  I have a Japanese camera.           ....................
5  She has a bath every day.           ....................
6  They have lunch at 12.30            ....................
7  He has a headache.                  ....................
8  They have a garden.                 ....................
9  We have a computer at home.         ....................
10 I have a penfriend in New Zealand.  ....................
11 She has a very good job.            ....................
12 We have three children.             ....................
13 They have a big house.              ....................
14 I have a brother.                   ....................
15 We have a dog.                      ....................

## 3 Make negative sentences

*Make negative sentences. Put the* <u>underlined</u> *words in the right order.*

**Example:**
She is very poor.    doesn't / have / any money / she
She is very poor.    She doesn't have any money.

1  The fridge is empty.   <u>any food / don't / we / have</u>
2  I don't like animals.  <u>we / any pets / have / don't</u>
3  I'm on holiday.        <u>don't / I / any homework / have</u>
4  We're in a hurry.      <u>don't / any time / have / we</u>
5  You can't have toast.  <u>don't / any bread / we / have</u>
6  It's a very small
   village                <u>doesn't / any shops / it / have</u>
7  She's unhappy.         <u>doesn't / good / have / job / a / she</u>
8  He's always angry      <u>any / he / friends / have / doesn't</u>
9  I don't like this
   coffee                 <u>any / sugar / have / it / doesn't / in / it</u>
10 She's at the shops     <u>doesn't / milk or bread/ she / any / have</u>

## 4 Make questions

**Example:**
*Do*    they   *have*   a car?
*Does*  he     *have*   a cat?

1  .......... you .......... a headache?
2  .......... he .......... an interesting job?
3  .......... they .......... a garden?
4  .......... she .......... short hair?
5  .......... you .......... lunch at home?
6  .......... he .......... a motorbike?
7  .......... we .......... food in the fridge?
8  .......... they .......... a holiday every year?
9  .......... you .......... a pen?
10 .......... you .......... a penfriend in Australia?

## 5 Complete the dialogues

*Complete these dialogues with* have, has, don't have *or* doesn't have.

**Example:**
**Donna:**   I *have* two tickets for a concert tonight. Can you come with me?
**Paul:**    No, I'm sorry. I *don't have* time. I *have* a lot of work to do.

1  **Tina:**    Do you .......... any brothers or sisters?
   **Philip:**  I .......... three brothers but I .......... any sisters.
2  **Sam:**     Do you .......... any pets?
   **Mary:**    We .......... 15 dogs, 7 cats and a parrot.
   **Sam:**     Do you .......... a holiday every year?
   **Mary:**    A holiday? With 23 animals in the house! No, we .......... any holidays!
3  **Oliver:**  Do you .......... tea with your breakfast?
   **Laura:**   We .......... tea or coffee. We only drink fruit juice in the morning.
4  **Gina:**    Is Tim OK?
   **Tessa:**   Not really. He .......... a headache and he .......... a cold.
   **Gina:**    I'm not surprised! It's the middle of winter. It's -3°C. There's 50 centimetres of snow. But every morning he .......... a swim in the river and then walks home in his T-shirt!

# UNIT 4 *have got*
## He has got five children

## FORM

1 Look at these sentences.

He **has got** five children.

They **have got** a new boss – they don't like her!

**Has** she **got** a new car?

**Have** you **got** a headache?

This is how we use *have got* and *has got* in the simple present.

**POSITIVE**

Subject + *have* / *has got*

**Long form:**

| | |
|---|---|
| I / You / We / They | have got |
| He / She / It | has got |

**Short form:**

| | |
|---|---|
| I've / You've / We've / They've | got |
| He's / She's / It's | got |

**I've got** a headache.

She **has got** red hair.

**They've got** three cars.

**Note:**

The short form is more common in conversation.

**NEGATIVE**

Subject + *have not* / *has not* + got

| | |
|---|---|
| I / You / We / They | have not got (haven't got) |
| He / She / It | has got (hasn't got) |

*I* **haven't got** the keys!

*Jack* **hasn't got** a computer.

**Note:**

The short form is more common in conversation.

**QUESTIONS**

*Have* / *has* + subject + *got*?

| | |
|---|---|
| Have I / you / we / they | got? |
| Has he / she / it | got? |

**Have** you **got** a headache?

**Has** Tony **got** a CD player?

## USE

1 *Have got* and *has got* are very similar to *have* and *has*.

Look at the uses of *have* and *has* in Unit 3. We can replace *have* and *has* with *have got* and *has got* for uses B, C and D.

We can use *have* / *has got* to talk about

**A** our families and people we know

He **has got** two sons, four daughters and twenty-three grandchildren.

**I've got** a penfriend in India.

**We've got** a new teacher. She speaks five languages!

**B** how we look and how we feel

**He's got** red hair.

**She's got** beautiful eyes.

**I've got** a cold. I'm not going to work today.

**C** things we possess

**They've got** a little house by the sea.

**She's got** a lot of money.

**I've got** a swimming pool.

In these sentences there is no difference between the way we use *have* / *has* and the way we use *have* / *has got*. But in British English we normally use *have got* and *has got* to express these ideas.

2 But there are times when only *have* / *has* are possible.

We do not use *have* / *has got* when we talk about the things we do regularly. For this reason, we use *have* / *has* to talk about

| actions | to have a bath, |
| | to have a swim |

and

| what we eat and drink | to have tea, |
| | to have lunch |

We say

*I have a swim before breakfast.*

(not *I've got a swim before breakfast.*)

*I have three cups of tea every day.*

(not *I've got three cups of tea a day.*)

---

### 1 Complete the sentences

*Complete the sentences with* have got *or* has got.

**Example:**

I *have got* two sisters.

1 My cat .......... green eyes.

2 He .......... a wonderful job.

3 She .......... orange hair!

4 Mike and Tessa .......... four children.

5 We .......... a flat near the post office.

6 She .......... twelve grandchildren.

7 He .......... a new camera.

8 I .......... a cold. I'm staying in bed today.

9 They .......... a lot of friends.

10 He .......... a very old car.

## 2 Make the sentences negative

*Make the sentences negative. Use* haven't got *or* hasn't got.

**Example:**

I've got a motorbike.    *I haven't got a motorbike.*

1 She's got a dog.
2 I've got an Italian car.
3 We've got a computer in our office.
4 He's got white hair.
5 She's got a headache.
6 They've got a garden.
7 I've got a penfriend in Australia.
8 We've got a swimming pool at our school.
9 She's got a radio in her car.
10 We've got a cinema in our village.

## 3 Make sentences

*Make sentences. Put the* underlined *words in the right order.*

**Example:**

I can't tell you the time.  I / a watch / got / haven't
I can't tell you the time.  *I haven't got a watch*.

1 I can't drive you to the station. I / a car / got / haven't
2 He can't go to Brazil. he / a passport / got / hasn't
3 You can't go to the concert. a ticket / haven't / you / got
4 It's a very small village. a post office / got / it / hasn't
5 We can't phone her. her number / got / we / haven't
6 They can't post the letter. a stamp / got / they haven't

## 4 Make questions

**Example:**

*Have* they *got* a car?
*Has* he *got* a dog?

1 .......... you .......... a cold?
2 .......... she .......... a good job?
3 .......... they .......... a big garden?
4 .......... she .......... long hair?
5 .......... she .......... a bicycle?
6 .......... we .......... any milk in the fridge?
7 .......... they .......... many friends?
8 .......... she .......... a pen?

9 .......... you .......... a question?
10 .......... you .......... the answer?

## 5 Complete the story

*Complete the story. Write* has got, have got, hasn't got *or* haven't got. *Use a negative when you see* not *in brackets,* (not). *The first one has been done for you.*

### One man and his dog

Mr Taylor has got a problem. He (**1**) *has got* a very large dog. The dog (**2**) .......... big teeth. Everybody likes Mr Taylor and he (**3**) .......... many friends, but his friends say they (**4**) .......... (not) time to visit his house.

Mr and Mrs Saunders (**5**) .......... two problems. They (**6**) .......... a small café near the station. The café is clean and the coffee is cheap, but they (**7**) .......... (not) many customers. The café (**8**) .......... twelve tables but today, for example, they (**9**) .......... only one customer. And it is always like this. So, Mr and Mrs Saunders are poor. And this is the second problem. Their daughter, Francesca, wants a dog to play with in the park. But Mr and Mrs Saunders (**10**) .......... (not) any money. So they can't buy a dog and their daughter is very sad.

The one customer who is sitting in Mr and Mrs Saunders' restaurant is Mr Taylor, the man who (**11**) .......... the big dog with the big teeth.

Mr Taylor is talking to Mr and Mrs Saunders. 'I (**12**) .......... a problem,' he says. 'I like my friends and I love my dog. My dog is a good dog. It's friendly and kind. But it (**13**) .......... big teeth and my friends are afraid.'

'We (**14**) .......... problems too,' Mr Saunders says. 'We (**15**) .......... a café but we (**16**) .......... (not) many customers. So we (**17**) .......... (not) the money to buy a dog for Francesca to play with in the park.'

So, here is a question. What can they do? Mr Taylor (**18**) .......... a dog. The dog (**19**) .......... big teeth. Mr Taylor (**20**) .......... lots of friends. He wants to see his friends. And they want to see him. But they are afraid of the dog because the dog (**21**) .......... big teeth. Mr and Mrs Saunders (**22**) .......... a café. But the café (**23**) .......... (not) any customers. And so their daughter (**24**) .......... (not) a dog to play with in the park.

It's Saturday and Mrs Saunders is smiling. She (**25**) .......... an idea that will make everyone happy. What do you think it is? Have you got the same idea? Look at page A of the Answer Key to see what they do.

## *There is / there are*

## There's a spider in the bath!

## FORM AND USE

**1** Look at these sentences.
**There's** *a good film on TV tonight.*
**There are** *twelve months in a year.*
**Is there** *a post office near here?*
**Are there** *good shops in your town?*
We often use *there* and the verb *to be* (*is, are, was, were* and *will be*) together to introduce a subject.
*There + to be + subject*
**There is** *a dog in the garden.*
**There are** *two girls in the café.*
**2** We use *there is* (*there's*) before a singular noun.
*Help me!* **There's** *a spider in the bath!*
and *there are* (*there're*) before a plural noun.
*There are* **100 centimetres** *in a metre.*
**Note:**
We normally use *there's* (the short form of *there is*) in conversation.
We sometimes use *there're* (the short form of *there are*) in conversation.
**3** Add *not* (*n't*) for the negative.
**There isn't** *a spider in the bath! That's a piece of soap!*
**There aren't** *many tourists here in the winter.*

**4** Put *is* or *are* at the beginning of the sentence to make a question.
**Is there** *a computer in Fred's bedroom?*
**Are there** *good beaches in Brighton?*
**5** We often give a short answer to questions with *is there* and *are there.*
**Is there** *a post office near here?*
*Yes, there is. / No, there isn't.*
**Are there** *big mountains in your country?*
*Yes, there are. No, there aren't.*
**6** We can add the word *any* to make the sentence stronger.
**There isn't any** *food in the fridge! Let's go to a restaurant.*
**There aren't any** *cheap restaurants near here. Let's eat at home!*
*There isn't any* + uncountable nouns
(like *food, work* and *sugar*)
*There aren't any* + countable nouns
(like *cars, books* and *bananas*)
(*See* Unit 30 for more about countable and uncountable nouns.)

---

**1** **Complete the sentences**

*This is Mark's bedroom. Complete the sentences with* there's a, there's an *or* there are.
**Examples:**
*There's a* bed.
*There are* two chairs.

1 .................... table near the window.
2 .................... computer.
3 .................... three postcards on the shelf.
4 .................... posters on the wall.
5 .................... shoes everywhere!
6 .................... book on the table.
7 .................... five pencils in a cup.
8 .................... football on the floor.

*Now write eight sentences about your bedroom. Use* there's a, there's an *and* there are. (See *Unit 24 for more about* a *and* an.)

**2** **Fill in the gaps**

*Fill in the gaps in this advertisement for Brighton, a holiday town 80 kilometres from London. Use* there's a, there's an *or* there are.
**Examples:**
*There's a* theatre – come and see a show!
*There are* great shops!

**(1)** .......... four beautiful beaches. **(2)** .......... good restaurants and **(3)** .......... five cinemas – come and see a film. **(4)** .......... interesting museum and, of course, **(5)** .......... good hotels, all near the beach. **(6)** .......... beautiful park near the city centre and **(7)** .......... ten car parks! **(8)** .......... market for fruit and vegetables. **(9)** .......... old lighthouse. Go there by boat! **(10)** .......... information centre at the train station – we can help you 24 hours a day!

## 3 Make questions

*Write* Is there *or* Are there *to make questions.*

**Example:**

*Is there* a bank near here?

1 .................... a football match on TV tonight?
2 .................... any good shops in your town?
3 .................... a swimming pool at your school?
4 .................... a television in your kitchen?
5 .................... a computer in your classroom?
6 .................... a famous person in your family?
7 .................... any taxis at the station?
8 .................... 29 days in February this year?
9 .................... any interesting museums in your country?
10 .................... an apple tree in your garden?

## 4 Make questions and answers

*Your brother is 7 years old. He is asking you some questions about the moon. Make questions and give short answers.*

**Examples:**

*Is there a* swimming pool on the moon? No, there isn't.
*Are there* any rivers on the moon? Yes, there are.

1 .......... mountains on the moon?          Yes, ..............
2 .......... car parks on the moon?          No, ..............
3 .......... elephants on the moon?          No, ..............
4 .......... an airport on the moon?         No, ..............
5 .......... seas on the moon?               Yes, ..............
6 .......... boats on the moon?              No, ..............
7 .......... a train station on the moon?    No, ..............
8 .......... deserts on the moon?            Yes, ..............
9 .......... camels on the moon?             No, ..............
10 .......... a school on the moon?          No, ..............
11 .......... any teachers on the moon?      No, ..............
12 .......... any homework on the moon?      No, ..............

## 5 Complete the sentences

*Complete the sentences with* there isn't any *or* there aren't any.

**Examples:**

*There isn't any* sugar in my tea!
*There aren't any* people in the street. It's very cold.

1 .................... bread in the kitchen.
2 .................... pens on the table.
3 .................... water! I can't wash up!
4 .................... trains to Tokyo today.
5 .................... supermarkets in our town.
6 .................... deserts in my country. It rains all the time!
7 .................... big mountains in my country.
8 .................... noise in the house. The children are at school!
9 .................... letters for you today. Sorry!
10 .................... more questions in this exercise.

## 6 Complete the sentences with *there is* or *there are*

*Solve the riddles! What is it?*

**Riddle 1**

It often has a bright jacket and inside **(1)** ..............
lots of sheets. **(2)** .............. lots of things like it.
**(3)** .............. old ones and new ones. They are friends.
In some of the friends, **(4)** .............. a lot of photographs, but **(5)** .............. (not) any in this one,
because it says a lot. What is it? **(6)**

**Riddle 2**

In some of them **(7)** .............. a lot of openings and in
some of them **(8)** .............. only two or three.
**(9)** .............. always one way into their inside like a
mouth, and inside **(10)** .............. a lot of other
'mouths'. They are like big boxes and inside
**(11)** .............. a lot of small boxes. People stay in
them. In a lot of them **(12)** .............. fires for the winter in cold countries. In the hot countries, they stay
open all the time. **(13)** .............. a cover for the rain
on all of them. What are they? **(14)**

**Riddle 3**

On all of them **(15)** .............. four legs. **(16)** ..............
families of them all over the world. **(17)** ..............
people in every country who look after them.
**(18)** .............. some black and white ones, and
**(19)** .............. some brown and white ones. On the
men **(20)** .............. two large bones by their ears.
What are they? **(21)**

Now write some riddles for your friends!

## Present Simple 1: Positive and Negative
### I work; I don't work

## FORM

Look at these sentences.
*I **live** in Barcelona.*
*My brother **works** for Coca Cola.*
*He **doesn't drink** coffee.*
These verbs are in the present simple.
**POSITIVE**

| I / You / We / They | eat |
| He / She / It | eats |

**1** To make the third person singular (the *he*, *she* and *it* form), add -*s* to most verbs.
*He play**s** the guitar.*
*She like**s** football.*
*This computer make**s** a lot of noise.*
**2** We normally add -*es* to verbs that end in -*ss*, -*o*, -*sh*, -*ch* or -*x*.
*She miss**es** the bus every day!*
*He go**es** to the cinema three times a week.*
*Jenny wash**es** her hair with French shampoo.*

*My dog watch**es** me when I eat breakfast.*
*Tony fix**es** our washing machine.*
**NEGATIVE**
When we make negative sentences in present simple, we put *do not* or *does not* before the base verb. We do not add -*s* to the base verb.

| I / You / We / They | do not (don't) | eat |
| He / She / It | does not (doesn't) | eat |

**Notes:**
**1** We normally use the short form of the negative in conversation.
*I **don't** understand.*
*He **doesn't** speak Italian.*
**2** We always use an infinitive after *do*, *do not* (*don't*) and *does not* (*doesn't*).

## USE

**1** We use the present simple
**A** to talk about the present
*They **live** in a small house near the sea.*
**B** for things that are always true
*Cats **like** milk.*
**C** for things that happen every day or things that happen regularly
*I **drink** tea every afternoon.*
*She **plays** tennis five times a week.*
**D** to talk about the jobs we do

*I'm a shop assistant. I **work** in a bookshop.*
**2** We often use the present simple with words like *never*, *sometimes* and *always* to talk about our lives.
*I **never eat** meat. I'm a vegetarian.*
*I **sometimes eat** meat. But meat is very expensive these days.*
*He **always eats** meat. He's a butcher!*

(See Unit 36 for more about frequency adverbs like *never*, *sometimes* and *always*.)

---

### 1  Complete the sentences

*Complete the sentences. Add* -s *or* -es.
**Example:**
He love*s* sugar.
She watch*es* too much television!

1 She play .......... golf at the weekend.
2 He drink .......... three litres of water every day!
3 She drive .......... a Korean car.
4 He finish .......... work at about 5 o'clock.
5 It get .......... very cold here in the winter.
6 My cat like .......... to sleep in front of the fire.
7 The shop open .......... at 9 and close .......... at 6.
8 Sally go .......... to the mountains three or four times a year.

9 He wash .......... his car every Saturday.
10 She walk .......... to school if she miss .......... the bus.
11 My brother live .......... in Canada.
12 When she make .......... a mistake, she smile .......... When I make a mistake, she get .......... angry!

### 2  Match the sentences

*Add* -s *or* -es *to the verb in B. Then match the sentences in A and B.*

| A | | B |
|---|---|---|
| 1  Tim's a fisherman. | a) | She type .......... letters all day. |
| 2  Paula's a teacher. | b) | He look .......... after 123 cows! |

3 Jackie's an artist.  c) She work .......... in a hospital.

4 Kelly's a secretary.  d) He go .......... to sea.

5 My uncle is a farmer.  e) She teach .......... at my school.

6 Karen's a doctor.  f) She paint .......... in a studio.

7 Antonio's a chef.  g) He work .......... in a garage.

8 Jack's a mechanic.  h) He cook .......... food in a restaurant.

## 3 Fill in the gaps

*Mr Thompson works in an office in Glasgow. Here he talks about what he does every day. Fill in the gaps with verbs from the box. The first one has been done for you.*

| | | | |
|---|---|---|---|
| are | arrive | brush | dream |
| drink | eat | feed | have |
| leave | lives | look | make |
| put | read | shines | sleep |
| talk | telephone | watch | write |

### My day

At 7.21 my alarm clock rings and I wake up. I hate my alarm clock! It makes too much noise. I get up at 7.30 and (1) *make* my bed.

Then I (2) .................... a shower and brush my teeth. I get dressed and have breakfast. I always
(3) .................... three eggs and five pieces of toast. I
(4) .................... two cups of tea and then I
(5) .................... my teeth again. I (6) ....................
some milk in a bowl for my dog, and at 8.30 I
(7) .................... the house and catch the bus to work.
I (8) .................... at the office at about 9 and drink a cup of tea. I eat some biscuits and (9) .................... out of the window. Then I have a rest.
At lunchtime I eat a sandwich and (10) ....................
the newspaper. At around 3.30 I take off my shoes and
(11) .................... for twenty minutes, sometimes twenty-five minutes, sometimes half an hour. I (12)
.................... two or three letters and (13) ....................
my sister who (14) .................... in Australia. We (15)
.................... for fifteen minutes. She always tells me about the weather. There (16) .................... three kinds of weather in Australia – hot, very hot and very, very hot!
I leave the office at about 4.30. When I get home I (17)

.................... the dog and (18) .................... TV. At 11.00, I make a hot water bottle and go to bed. The moon (19) .................... in the sky and I sleep. I (20) .................... about my holidays. Then at 7.21 my alarm clock rings.
**Now write 10 sentences about your day.**

## 4 Make negative sentences

*Make negative sentences with* doesn't.
**Example:**
Jim's a postman. He / not / like dogs.
*Jim's a postman. He doesn't like dogs.*

1 Jenny's a vegetarian. She / not / eat meat.
2 We're moving to Tunisia. My husband / not / like cold weather.
3 He can't understand the film. He / not / speak Arabic.
4 Mark's looking for a new job. He / not / like his boss.
5 She can't post the letter. She / not / have a stamp.
6 She can't buy new shoes. She / not / have any money.
7 Please use the stairs. The lift / not / work.
8 It's an electric car. It / not / use petrol.
9 You talk to him. He / not / listen to me.
10 Shall we walk to the station? The bus / not / stop here.

## 5 Make negative sentences

*Make negative sentences with* don't.
**Example:**
Please speak slowly. I / not / understand English very well.
*Please speak slowly. I don't understand English very well.*

1 Can you tell me the time please? I / not / have a watch.
2 I can't drive you to the party. I / not / have a car.
3 Why are you eating a pizza? You / not / like cheese.
4 I'm tired. I / not / want to go out tonight.
5 That's a difficult question. I / not / know the answer.
6 It's a very small house. We / not / have a garden.
7 I can't marry you. I / not / love you.
8 I can't buy you a present. I / not / have any money.
9 I'm a doorman. I / not / like the rain.
10 I'm a snowman. I / not / like the sun.

# UNIT 7   Present Simple 2: Questions
## Do you like French food?

## FORM

**1**   Look at these sentences.
**Do** I **need** a visa for America?
**Do** you **like** French food?
**Does** it **rain** a lot in Scotland?
**Do** they **have** any children?
These are question forms of the present simple.

**2**   *do* + subject + base verb or
*does* + subject + base verb
We always use the base verb after *do* and *does*.
**Does** this bus **go** to the station? Not *Does this bus goes to the station?*

| Do | I / you / we / they | want | an ice-cream? |
| Does | he / she / it | want | an ice-cream? |

## USE

**1**   We often put *do* or *does* in a short answer to questions
*Do you play the guitar?*     *Yes, I do. / No, I don't.*
*Does your brother play the guitar?*     *Yes, he does. / No, he doesn't.*

**2**   We often put words like *when, where, why* and *what* before *do* and *does*
**When** does the film start?
**Where** do you live?
**Why** do birds fly north in the winter?
**What** does this word mean?

---

### 1   Make questions with *do* or *does*

**Example:**

you / play / the guitar          *Do you play the guitar?*

your brother / play the guitar          *Does your brother play the guitar?*

1   you / like eggs ......................?
2   you / watch a lot of TV ......................?
3   he / come to work by bus ......................?
4   you / take sugar in your tea ......................?
5   she / want a dog ......................?
6   you / have any brothers or sisters ......................?
7   you / have any money ......................?
8   this train / go to Tokyo ......................?
9   you / live near the sea ......................?
10  you / know / her telephone number ......................?
11  you / own a car ......................?
12  he / know the answers ......................?

### 2   Make questions and answers

*Make questions and give short answers.*
**Examples:**
you / need the car tonight
*Do you need the car tonight?*
Yes, I *do.*

he / understand / the question
*Does he understand the question?*
No, he *doesn't.*

1   you / like my dress          No, I ..........
2   you / like Indian food          Yes, I ..........
3   you / eat a lot of fruit          No, I ..........
4   Sally / play tennis          No, she ..........
5   you / want to hear a joke          No, I ..........
6   you / have a computer at home          Yes, I ..........
7   you / make your own bread          No, I ..........
8   your sister / like her job          Yes, she ..........
9   we / have any stamps          No, we ..........
10  you / love me          Yes, I ..........
11  you / want a cup of tea          No, I ..........
12  they / like chocolate          Yes, they ..........

## 3 Write questions and match

*Write questions with* do *and* does *in A. Then match the questions with the answers in B.*

**Example question:**

what / you / do          *What do you do?*

| A | | B | |
|---|---|---|---|
| 1 | where / you / work | a) | I don't have a car. |
| 2 | when / you / start work | b) | We live near the station. |
| 3 | where / you / live | c) | Just before nine. |
| 4 | what / you / have for breakfast | d) | Dog food! |
| 5 | what / your dog / have for breakfast | e) | Toast and tea. |
| 6 | what / your brother / do | f) | Let's go to the cinema. |
| 7 | what / you / want to do tonight | g) | He's a teacher. |
| 8 | why / you / walk to work | h) | I work in a shoe shop. |

## 4 Make questions

*a) Put the words for each sentence in the right order and b) make them into questions.*

**Example:**

way Santa Fe know you the

ANSWER: a)*You know the way to Santa Fe.*

     b) *Do you know the way to Santa Fe?*

1  moves sun the the round earth
2  you I love
3  Venice train stops this at
4  holiday golf play on you
5  does the always exercises she all
6  colour that they of house the like
7  late always arrives she
8  today you ill feel
9  that on they books course read interesting
10  £300 cost chairs those
11  sells bread shop that
12  true tells film war that the of the story
13  car fast your goes
14  work enjoys he company at that the
15  nice she very got friends has
16  angry it you makes
17  Rome you in live
18  'pop' she listens to music
19  moon go they to want to be
20  East in rises sun the the

## 5 Complete the story

*Complete the story with* do, don't, does *or* doesn't. *The first one has been done for you.*

An elephant goes into an Italian restaurant and sits down at a table. A waiter arrives and says, 'Can I help you sir?'

'Yes,' says the elephant. '**(1)** *Do* you have any coffee?'

'We **(2)** .......... have coffee,' the waiter replies. 'We only have tea.' 'I'll have a cup of tea then,' the elephant says, and the waiter goes to the kitchen.

The manager of the restaurant is standing in the kitchen. He is not happy.

'What **(3)** .......... the elephant want?' the manager asks.

'He wants a cup of coffee,' the waiter replies.

'But we **(4)** .......... have coffee,' the manager says. 'We only have tea.'

'I know,' the waiter replies. ' I told the elephant we **(5)** .......... have coffee. I'm getting him a tea.'

'**(6)** .......... the elephant have any money?' the manager says.

'I **(7)** .......... know,' the waiter replies. '**(8)** .......... elephants have money? They **(9)** .......... have pockets!'

'Well, give him the tea,' the manager says. 'If he **(10)** .......... have any money he can wash the dishes for us.'

So, the waiter returns with the tea, and says, 'Here's your tea sir, and here's the bill for £3.50.'

The elephant drinks the tea but he **(11)** .......... look very happy.

'Is the tea OK, sir?' the waiter asks.

'No, says the elephant. You put milk and sugar in my tea. **(12)** .......... you know anything about elephants? Elephants **(13)** .......... like milk and they **(14)** .......... like sugar. We **(15)** .......... drink tea with milk and sugar!'

'I'm sorry, sir,' the waiter says. 'I **(16)** .......... know much about elephants. We **(17)** .......... see many elephants in this restaurant.'

'That **(18)** .......... surprise me,' the elephant replies. 'Your tea's expensive.'

# UNIT 8  Present Continuous 1: with Present Meaning
## I am working

## FORM

Look at these sentences.
*She **is learning** Chinese.*
*You **are reading** this book*
*You **aren't playing** football.*
***Are** you **working** hard?*
These verbs are in the present continuous.
We make the present continuous with the verb *to be*
and the *-ing* form of the verb.

**POSITIVE**

| I | am ('m) | coming |
| He / She / It | is ('s) | coming |
| We / You / They | are ('re) | coming |

**NEGATIVE**

| I | am not ('m not) | coming |
| He / She / It | is not ('s not / isn't) | coming |
| We / You / They | are not ('re not / aren't) | coming |

**QUESTIONS**

| Am | I | coming? |
| Is | he / she / it | coming? |
| Are | you / we / they | coming? |

**The -*ing* form of the verb**

**1**  Add -*ing* for most verbs.
*talk – talking*
*eat – eating*
*drink – drinking*
*ask – asking*

**2**  For verbs that end in *-e*, drop the *-e* then add *-ing*.
*come – coming*
*write – writing*
*dance – dancing*
*love – loving*

**3**  For verbs that end in vowel + consonant, double the last letter.
*get – getting*
*sit – sitting*
*shop – shopping*
*stop – stopping*

**Note:**
We normally use the short form in conversation.
*He's talking.*
*They're not listening.*

## USE

We use the present continuous
**A**  to talk about what is happening at the moment
*Be quiet! **The baby is sleeping**.*
*Take an umbrella. **It's raining**.*
**B**  for things that are temporary
*We're on holiday. We **are renting** a car for a few days.*

*I'm **staying** in a hotel this week.*
**C**  for things that started in the past and are continuing now
*She's **studying** medicine. She wants to be a doctor.*
*I'm **learning** the piano. It's very difficult!*
***What** are you **doing**?*

### 1  Write the *-ing* form of these verbs

1  wash *washing*
2  talk ..........
3  go ..........
4  come ..........
5  take ..........
6  make ..........
7  move ..........
8  shop ..........
9  stop ..........
10  plan ..........
11  sit ..........
12  get ..........
13  break ..........
14  laugh ..........
15  stay ..........

### 2  Complete the sentences

*Complete the sentences with the -ing form of the verbs in the box. The first one has been done for you.*

| answer | cook | learn | play | read |
| sing | talk | tell | try | watch | write |

1  What's she doing? She's *watching* TV.
2  Listen! She's .............. an old Spanish song. It's beautiful.
3  I'm .............. a really interesting book at the moment.
4  He's .............. a letter to his sister. He's .............. her about his new job.
5  What's he doing? He's .............. the piano.
6  What are you doing? I'm .............. your question!
7  He's in the kitchen, .............. dinner.

8 Where is Jane? She's ............... to her sister on the phone.
9 We're ............... French before our holiday there.
10 I'm ............... to lift this box, but it's very heavy.

## 3 Write sentences

*It's Saturday afternoon. You are looking out of your window. Write sentences about what you see. Use the present continuous.*
**Examples:**
Bill / wash his car
*Bill is washing his car.*
Some children / play football in the park
*Some children are playing football in the park.*

1 Mrs Johnson / sit in her garden
2 Mr Johnson / play the piano
3 The sun / shine
4 Three dogs / swim in the river
5 A cat / sleep in a tree
6 Some men / talk near the post office
7 Dr Jones / work in her office
8 A policeman / walk down the street
9 Fiona / take a photograph of her brother
10 Some boys / eat ice-cream near the school
11 Some birds / fly over the park.
12 A little girl / ride her bicycle.
13 Jane and Peter / drink coffee in the bar.
14 Maria / shop for her dinner.
15 My son / talk to his friends on the phone.

## 4 Write the dialogue

*Your brother Fred telephones you and asks you lots of questions. You are very busy but try to be nice to him. Write the dialogue.*
**Example:**
**Fred:** you / watch TV
*Are you watching TV?*
**You:** No, / I not watch TV. I / work, Fred
*No, I'm not watching TV. I'm working, Fred.*

**1**
**Fred:** you / read a magazine
**You:** No, I not read a magazine. I / read a book about English grammar, Fred.

**2**
**Fred:** you / eat chocolate
**You:** No, I not eat chocolate. I / try to understand the present continuous, Fred.

**3**
**Fred:** You / listen to the radio
**You:** No, / I not listen to the radio. I / do my homework, Fred.

**4**
**Fred:** You / play the piano
**You:** No, / I not play the piano. I / write the answers to this exercise, Fred.

**5**
**Fred:** You / listening to me
**You:** No, / I not listen to you. I / put down the phone, Fred. Goodbye!

## 5 Write questions and answers

**Example:**
What / you / do
*What are you doing?*
I / clean / my shoes
*I am cleaning my shoes.*

1 What / you / eat
I / eat / a sandwich
2 What / she / watch
She / watch / a film
3 What / you / write
I / write / a letter to my cousin
4 What / you / drink
I / drink / some lemonade
5 What / they / read
They / read / Grammar Workbook 1
6 What / she / do
She / make / bread in the kitchen
7 What / you / look for
I / look for / my yellow socks
8 Why / you / laugh
The cat / eat / your dinner!
9 Where / he / go
He / go / to the library
10 What / they / listen to
They / listen to / the radio

# Present Continuous 2: with Future Meaning
## He's arriving tomorrow

## FORM

**1** Look at these sentences.
***She's going*** *on holiday tomorrow.*
***They're moving*** *to a new house next year.*
***Are you coming*** *to the party tonight?*
These verbs are in the present continuous. But here we are not talking about the present. We are talking about the future (tomorrow, next year, tonight).
This is the second use of the present continuous.
**2** The verb form is the same as when we talk about the present. (*See* Unit 8.)
subject + *am / is / are* + the *-ing* form of the verb for a positive sentence

***I'm buying*** *a new bicycle tomorrow.*
subject + *am / 'm / is / 's / are / 're + not* + the *-ing* form of the verb for a negative sentence
***I'm not going*** *to the party. I've got toothache. I'm going to the dentist.*
*am / is / are* + subject + the *-ing* form of the verb for a question
***Are they meeting*** *Tim at the airport? He's arriving at 11.30.*

## USE

**1** We use the present continuous to talk about our plans for the future.
***I'm going*** *to university next year.*
***We're getting*** *married in October.*
**2** We often put words like *when* and *how* at the beginning of a present continuous question to ask for information about the future.

***When are you going*** *to Sweden? On Monday or Tuesday?*
***When are we playing*** *tennis? This week or next week?*
***How are we getting*** *to the airport? By taxi?*

### 1 Write sentences

*This is Sally Thompson's diary for tomorrow. Write sentences about her day. Use the present continuous. The first one has been done for you.*

| | |
|---|---|
| 7.00 a.m. | take the dog for a walk |
| 8.00 a.m. | have breakfast |
| 9.00 a.m. | go to the bank for some money |
| 10.30 a.m. | make some bread |
| 11.30 a.m. | buy some fruit at the greengrocer's |
| 1.00 p.m. | meet Joanna for lunch |
| 3.00 p.m. | wash some shirts |
| 3.30 p.m. | take the car to the garage |
| 5.00 p.m. | clean the windows in the kitchen |
| 6.45 p.m. | play squash with Jenny |
| 8.15 p.m. | cook dinner for the family |
| 9.30 p.m. | wash up |
| 11.00 p.m. | have a shower |
| 11.30 p.m. | go to bed |
| 11.31 p.m. | go to sleep! |

*At 7 she's taking the dog for a walk.*
1 ................................................................
2 ................................................................

3 ................................................................
4 ................................................................
5 ................................................................
6 ................................................................
7 ................................................................
8 ................................................................
9 ................................................................
10 ...............................................................
11 ...............................................................
12 ...............................................................
13 ...............................................................
14 ...............................................................

*Now write ten sentences about what you are planning to do tomorrow.*

### 2 Write sentences

*It's January and you are making plans for the year. Write sentences to describe what you are doing in the next few months. Use the present continuous.*
**Example:**
February, I / fly to Jamaica for a holiday.
*In February I'm flying to Jamaica for a holiday.*

1. March, I / fish in Scotland.
2. April, I / learn German in Berlin.
3. May, I / take my boat down the Nile.
4. June, I / get engaged.
5. July, I / make a film in Hollywood.
6. August, I / walk from South Africa to Morocco.
7. September, I / get married.
8. October, we / climb Mount Kilimanjaro together.
9. November, we / buy a house.
10. December, I / sell my boat!

## 3  Write questions and answers

*Write questions and answers. Use the present continuous.*

**Example:**

When / you / do the exam?     I / do the exam in June

*When are you doing the exam?*   *I am doing the exam in June.*

1. When / she / go to Hong Kong?
   She / go / to Hong Kong on Tuesday.
2. When / the train / leave?
   The train / leave / at half past three.
3. When / you / play golf with Fred?
   We / play / tomorrow afternoon.
4. What / you / do / tomorrow?
   I / clean / the house.
5. When / you / meet your girlfriend?
   I / meet / her / at one o'clock.
6. Where / you / meet your uncle?
   I / meet / him / at a café.
7. What / you / do / tonight?
   I / wash / my hair.
8. Where / we / have / dinner tonight?
   We / have / dinner at that new Spanish restaurant near the river.
9. Why / you / not come to the party?
   I / study / for my exams.
10. Why / you / not study tonight?
    I / go / to a party!

## 4  Write questions and answers

*Write questions with* how *and the present continuous. Then write answers.*

**Example:**

How / he / get to the cinema?
*How is he getting to the cinema?*
He / there / by taxi
*He's getting there by taxi.*

1. How / we / get to the airport?
   We / there / by train
2. How / we / get to China?
   We / there / by plane
3. How / they / go to the island?
   They / there / by ferry
4. How / they / get to the top of the mountain?
   They / there / by the ski lift
5. How / the President / come to the meeting?
   She / here / by helicopter
6. How / you / go to the supermarket?
   I / there / by bus
7. How / you / get home?
   I / there / by car
8. How / I / get home?
   You / there / on foot!

## 5  Complete the dialogue

*Complete the dialogue by putting the verb in brackets in the correct form of the present continuous.*

**Jane:** What (**1** – do) you next week?
**Alice:** Well, I (**2** – go) to Paris; but Stan (**3** – come – not).
**Jane:** What (**4** – do) he?
**Alice:** He (**5** – paint) the kitchen and (**6** – teach) at school.
**Jane:** (**7** – Visit) you any friends?
**Alice:** Yes. I (**8** – stay) with some old school friends. They work in Paris.
They work for an American company. But next year, they (**9** – start) their own business.
**Jane:** (**10** – change) Stan schools next term?
**Alice:** No. He (**11** – stop) teaching.
**Jane:** What (**12** – do) he?
**Alice:** Next year, he (**13** – study) again. Business Studies.
**Jane:** Why?
**Alice:** He (**14** – go) into business with my friends in Paris.
**Jane:** So, you (**15** – move) to Paris.
**Alice:** Yes. You usually go to France. (**16** – go) you this year?
**Jane:** No. Bill (**17** – work) in Berlin all through the summer. He (**18** – design) a new building for a small publishing company.
**Alice:** (**19** – build) he it as well?
**Jane:** Oh no. A big German building company (**20** – do) that.
**Alice:** Interesting work, though.
**Jane:** Yes. Well, enjoy Paris!

# UNIT 10 Present Simple v. Present Continuous
## She lives or She is living

In Units 6 and 7 we looked at the simple present. In Units 8 and 9 we looked at the present continuous. In this unit we are going to compare the two tenses.

## USE

**PRESENT SIMPLE**

1   For things that are always true
*She loves books.*
*She reads a lot.*
*We live in Manchester.*
*Do you live in Manchester?*

2   For things that are regular
*It snows here every winter.*
*Does it snow here every winter*

3   We often use frequency adverbs (*always, never sometimes*) with the present simple

**PRESENT CONTINUOUS**

1   For things that are happening now
*You are reading this book.*
*We are staying in a hotel for a few days.*
*Are you staying in a hotel?*

2   For things that are temporary
*Look! It's snowing!*

3   We do not use frequency adverbs with the present continuous. We use expressions like *for a few days, at the moment* and *this week*
*He **never** watches television.*
*He's watching television **at the moment**.*

**Note:**
There are some common verbs that we don't normally use in the present continuous. These verbs include *hate, know, like, love, mean, need, remember, think, believe, understand, want*
We normally use these verbs in the present simple.
*I hate cold weather.*    (not *I am hating cold weather.*)
*I love you.*    (not *I am loving you.*)

---

### 1   Make sentences

*Make sentences. Use the present simple or the present continuous.*

**Examples:**
He / read a newspaper at the moment
*He is reading a newspaper at the moment.*
He / read the same newspaper every day
*He reads the same newspaper every day.*

1   It / snow. Let's build a snowman.
2   It's very cold here. It / snow every day in the winter.
3   He / eat an apple every day.
4   She usually / start work at 8.30. But she / start at 9.00 today.
5   The sun / shine. Let's go to the beach.
6   In Japanese, 'mushi mushi' / mean / 'hello'.
7   My teacher / speak four languages.
8   He usually / go to bed at 10.00.
9   This grammar is very difficult! I need / some help!
10  He usually / wake up at 7.00. And he normally / go to work by bus. But he woke up at 8.33 this morning. So, today he / take a taxi!

### 2   Complete the sentences

*Complete the sentences. Write the verb in brackets in the present simple or the present continuous.*

**Example:**
He always *takes* (take) the dog for a walk before breakfast.
Edward is out at the moment. He *is taking* (take) the dog for a walk.

1   She .......... (hate) Italian food! She never .......... (eat) spaghetti. But her husband .... (love) Italian food. He .......... (cook) pizza every day!
2   He .......... (wash) his hair every day.
3   He's in the shower. He .......... (wash) his hair.
4   .......... (like) you jazz?
5   Listen! The baby .......... (cry)!
6   What .......... (mean) this word?
7   .......... (know) you her telephone number?
8   She .......... (study) grammar two hours a day.
9   They .......... (go) to the cinema once a week.
10  Hi, Jim. Thanks for calling! Listen, I .......... (have) lunch at the moment. Can I call you back?

*The questions in Revision Test 1 are about the grammar in Units 1–10. Choose the best answer, A, B or C.*

## UNITS 1-5

1  He ............... a teacher.
   A  am          B  is          C  are
2  They .................. French.
   A  'm          B  's          C  're
3  .................. cold today.
   A  It          B  Its         C  It's
4  .................. you ready?
   A  Am          B  Is          C  Are
5  .................. I right?
   A  Am          B  Is          C  Are
6  .................. these shoes expensive?
   A  Am          B  Is          C  Are
7  She .................. brown hair.
   A  has         B  is have     C  have
8  They .................. a small flat near the station.
   A  has         B  to have     C  have
9  He .................. a lot of money.
   A  doesn't have  B  don't have   C  doesn't has
10  We .................. a dog.
   A  doesn't have  B  don't have   C  don't has
11  .................. you have a headache?
   A  Does        B  Do          C  Is
12  They .................. four children.
   A  has got     B  have got    C  have get
13  He .................. a swim in the river every afternoon.
   A  has         B  has got     C  have
14  .................. she got a new bicycle?
   A  Has         B  Does she has  C  Have
15  There .................. a cat in the garden.
   A  am          B  is          C  are
16  There .................. any good films on TV tonight.
   A  'm not      B  isn't       C  aren't

## UNITS 6-7

17  She .................. the piano.
   A  play        B  is play     C  plays
18  He .................. his hair every day.
   A  wash        B  washs       C  washes
19  They .................. German.
   A  don't speak  B  don't speaks  C  doesn't speak
20  .................. a visa for America?
   A  Do need I   B  Does need I  C  Do I need
21  Does .................. to the station?
   A  go this bus  B  this bus go  C  goes this bus

22  .................. this word mean?
   A  Does what   B  What does   C  What do
23  Do you play the piano? Yes, .................. .
   A  I don't     B  do I        C  I do
24  Where ..................?
   A  do you live  B  live you    C  do live you

## UNITS 8-9

25  She .................. Japanese.
   A  learn       B  is learn    C  is learning
26  I .................. in a hotel for a few days.
   A  stay        B  am staying  C  stays
27  .................. to the party tonight?
   A  Come you    B  Are you     C  Are you
                                comeing        coming
28  Where ..................?
   A  going you   B  are you going  C  do you going
29  Why ..................?
   A  laughing he  B  is he        C  does he
                   laughing       laughing
30  She's .................. tomorrow.
   A  a new bicycle  B  buying      C  buy a new
      buying         a new bicycle    bicycle
31  How .................. to the airport tomorrow?
   A  getting we   B  are we        C  are we
                   geting          getting
32  When .................. to Hong Kong?
   A  are you going  B  going you   C  going you are
33  We .................. to the party. We're very tired.
   A  not going    B  isn't going   C  aren't going

## UNIT 10

34  It .................. here every winter.
   A  is snowing   B  snow         C  snows
35  I .................. a shower before breakfast.
   A  always have  B  am always    C  am always
                   have             having
36  We .................. cold weather.
   A  are hating   B  are hate     C  hate
37  What .................. ?
   A  does this    B  is meaning   C  is this word
      word mean      this word       meaning
38  He .................. the same newspaper every day.
   A  is reading   B  reading is   C  reads
39  We .................. for a few days.
   A  renting a car  B  are renting  C  a car rent
                     a car
40  .................. at the moment?
   A  Snows it     B  Does it snow  C  Is it snowing

# UNIT 11   The Imperative
## Come here!

## FORM

Look at these sentences.
*Come here!*
*Listen!*
*Sleep well!*
These are imperatives. The imperative is the base form
of the verb.
**POSITIVE**
We form imperative sentences
**1**   as one word
*Help! Stop! Look!*
**2**   with an object
*Help **me**!  Stop **the bus**!  Look at **that bird**!*
**3**   with two objects
*Give **me that pen**!  Pass **me the salt**!*

**Note:**
An imperative can sound strong.
*Open the bag!*
*Buy some milk!*
But we can add the word *please* to make it softer.
*Open the bag, please!*
*Buy some milk, please!*
**NEGATIVE**
For the negative form, we put *don't* at the beginning.
*Don't do that!*
*Don't touch the painting!*
*Don't eat and talk at the same time!*
**Note:**
The imperative cannot have a question form.

## USE

We use the imperative
**1**   to tell people what to do
*Come in! Sit down! Start work! Don't talk!*
**2**   to welcome people
*Come in and sit down. Take off your coat. Have a
coffee.*

**3**   for instructions
*Put the rice in the water and cook it for 20 minutes.*
**4**   to give advice
*Don't eat that bread. It's not fresh!*
*Drive carefully! The roads are wet.*

---

### 1   Complete the sentences

*Complete the sentences with the imperative form of the
verbs in the box.*

> be  bring  buy  have  give  fasten  help  hurry
> look  open  read  say  sleep  stay  take  turn

**Example:**
(in a grammar book)      *read* the examples!

**1**   (at the dentist's) .................. wide, please!
**2**   (at the doctor's) .................. aah!
**3**   (on a plane) .................. your seatbelts, please!
**4**   (on the street) .................. out! There's a car
coming!
**5**   (at the station) .................. up! The train is leaving
now.
**6**   (in the river) .................. me! I can't swim!
**7**   (to your dog) .................. there!
**8**   (to your friend) .................. a drink. I've got tea,
coffee or orange juice.
**9**   (to a taxi driver) .................. left here, please!

**10**   (at the end of the day) .................. well!
**11**   (in a restaurant) ...... me the menu, please.
**12**   (to a child) .................. careful. There a lot of cars
on the road.
**13**   (in the supermarket) .................. our soap now!
**14**   (at dinner) .................. the plates to the table,
please.
**15**   (in a shop) .................. me another bag, please.
I've got a lot to carry.

### 2   Make negative imperatives

*Mr Moody, the manager of a small hotel in Brighton, is
telling a guest family about the rules of the hotel. What
are Mr Moody's rules? Put the words in the right order
to make negative imperatives.*
**Example:**
that / don't / do!
*Don't do that!*

**1**   biscuits / in bed / don't / eat!
**2**   listen / to the radio / don't / after 10 o'clock!
**3**   don't / on the stairs / food / eat!

4 at breakfast / talk / don't!
5 use / hot water / don't / in the bath!
6 ask / me / don't / questions / any!
7 sleep / don't / open / with the window!
8 don't / the telephone / use!
9 forget / your key / don't!
10 after 11 o'clock / come in / don't / after!
11 anything / leave / in your room / don't!
12 don't / children / bring / to the hotel!
13 at dinner / ask for / don't / more food!
14 after 9.30 / don't / your room / stay in / in the morning!
15 forget / to enjoy / don't / your holiday!

## 3 Complete the recipe

*Fred has just written a book called* How to cook well. *On page 23 he tells us how to make a cheese sandwich. Complete the recipe with the imperative form of the verbs in the box. The first one has been done for you.*

buy cut dry eat find go open put say take wash

---

**Learn how to make a cheese and onion sandwich!**

**1** *Go* to the supermarket. .......... some bread, some cheese and an onion.
**2** .......... your hands with soap. Then .......... them.
**3** .......... the fridge. .......... out the butter. .......... a plate.
**4** .......... the cheese and the onion into small pieces.
**5** .......... the cheese and the onions and the butter on the bread.
**6** .......... the sandwich and .......... , 'Mmm, that was nice!'

23

---

## 4 Choose the right imperative

*There are three imperatives in the brackets. Choose the right one to complete the sentences.*
**Example:**
Put the potatoes into the water and *cook* (fly / jump / cook) them for 20 minutes.

1 Wash the dishes and then .................. (cook / eat / dry) them.
2 Go to the grocer's and .................. (drive / buy / telephone) some sugar.
3 Buy a newspaper and .................. (sing to / dance with / read) it.
4 Buy some new trousers and .................. (wear / talk to / understand) them.
5 Buy a banana and .................. (post / eat / marry) it.
6 Buy a grammar book and .................. (drink / study / play) it!
7 Go to the kitchen and .................. (make / throw / buy) a cup of tea.
8 Find your keys and .................. (break / drink / open) the door.
9 Go home and .................. (think / play / watch) television.
10 Find a new house and .................. (drop / cook / buy) it.

## 5 Match the parts

*Read the statements. Then match the parts in A and B to make responses. The first one has been done for you.*

|   |   | A | B |
|---|---|---|---|
| 1 | I'm going to bed | Sleep | of tea! |
| 2 | It's raining | Take my | window! |
| 3 | I like driving fast | Stop the | apples, please. |
| 4 | It's hot in here | Open the | old ones! |
| 5 | I'm thirsty | Drink a cup | well! |
| 6 | I've got toothache | Go to | down, please. |
| 7 | These shoes are uncomfortable. | Wear the | umbrella! |
| 8 | Is this seat free? | Yes, sit | the dentist! |
| 9 | I'm going to the greengrocer's | Buy some | car now! |

# UNIT 12 Past Tense of *to be*: *was / were*
## I was right; Were they cold?

## FORM

Look at these sentences.
*She* **was** *happy.*
*The photographs* **were** *beautiful.*
**Was** *it cold last night?*
**Were** *the bananas yellow or green?*
Remember how we talked about the present with *am*, *is* and *are* (Units 1 and 2). The verb *to be* also has two past forms, *was* and *were*.

### POSITIVE
Subject + *was / were*

| I / He / She / It | was right |
| You / We / They | were right |

*She* **was** *afraid.*
*They* **were** *at the cinema.*
**Note:**
There is no short form for the positive.

### NEGATIVE
subject + *was / were* + *not*

| I / He / She / It | was not (wasn't) right |
| You / We / They | were not (weren't) right |

*She* **wasn't** *afraid.*
*They* **weren't** *there.*
**Note:**
For the negative, we can use the long form (*I was not happy*) or the short form (*I wasn't happy*). The short form is much more common.

### QUESTIONS
*was / were* + subject

| Was | I / he / she / it | right? |
| Were | we / you / they | right? |

**Was** *it cold last night?*
**Were** *the trains fast?*

## USE

**1** We use *was* and *were* to talk about the past. For this reason, we often put words or phrases like *yesterday*, *three hours ago*, *last month* and *in 1950* with *was* and *were*.
*It was cold* **yesterday.**
*They were in Kenya* **in 1995.**

**2** We often use words like *when*, *where* and *who* before *was* and *were* for questions.
**When** *was breakfast?*
**Where** *were you?*
**When** *were they in Portugal?*

**3** We use *was* and *were* (like we use *am*, *is* and *are*) for

**A** jobs
*Leonardo da Vinci was a famous painter.*
**B** places
*She was in Manchester last week.*
**C** to describe things and people
*The bus was yellow.*
*The woman was very tall.*

**4** We use *it was* and *was it* to talk about
**A** the weather
*It was very hot in Morocco yesterday!*
*Was it hot in Canada?*
**B** the time
*It was 5.23 when the plane arrived.*

---

### 1 Write sentences

*Write the sentences in the past. Use* was *or* were.
**Example:**
I am hot.              *I was hot.*

| | Today | Yesterday |
|---|---|---|
| 1 | The flat is cold. | ................................... |
| 2 | The cafés are full. | ................................... |
| 3 | The bank isn't open. | ................................... |
| 4 | That question is easy. | ................................... |

5 They are tired. ...................................
6 The book is interesting. ...................................
7 The trains are slow. ...................................
8 The weather is good. ...................................
9 The radio is on. ...................................
10 The bags are very heavy. ...................................
11 The water is very cold. ...................................
12 The water isn't very hot. ...................................
13 He's very strong. ...................................
14 I'm very tired. ...................................
15 My boss is very friendly. ...................................

## 2 Ask questions

*Your brother went to a new restaurant yesterday. Ask him some questions using* was *and* were.

**Example:**

the food / good      *Was the food good?*

1 the restaurant / busy     ...............................?
2 the waiters / friendly     ...............................?
3 the knives and forks / clean     ...............................?
4 the soup / hot     ...............................?
5 the vegetables / fresh     ...............................?
6 the ice-cream / OK     ...............................?
7 the coffee / good     ...............................?
8 the meal / expensive     ...............................?

## 3 Put the words in the right order

*Put the words in the right order to make questions (A) and answers (B).*

**Example:**

When / your birthday / was?
*When was your birthday?*
yesterday / it / was
*It was yesterday.*

**A**

1 when / the party / was?
2 where / the party / was?
3 where / last night / you / were?
4 when / in New Zealand / you / were?
5 was / who / Michelangelo?
6 teacher / your first / was / who?

**B**

was / last night / it
at Tina's house / was / it
at home / I / was
there / in 1993 / were / we
painter / was / he / a famous
my / Mrs Heiber / was / first teacher

## 4 Complete the dialogue

*You saw a wonderful film yesterday. Your friend, Jackie, wants to know all about it. Complete the dialogue with* was *or* were *and an adjective from the box. The first two have been done for you.*

| cheap Chinese easy full funny short small |
| --- |

**Jackie:** *Was* the film long?
**You:** No, it *was short.*

**Jackie:** (1) ..................... the film Japanese?
**You:** No, it (2) .....................
**Jackie:** (3) ..................... it difficult to understand the story?
**You:** No, it (4) .....................
**Jackie:** (5) ..................... the story sad?
**You:** No, it (6) .....................
**Jackie:** (7) ..................... the cinema big?
**You:** No, it (8) .....................
**Jackie:** (9) ..................... the cinema empty?
**You:** No, it (10) .....................
**Jackie:** (11) ..................... the tickets expensive?
**You:** No, they (12) .....................

## 5 Complete the dialogues

*Complete the dialogues with* was, wasn't, were *or* weren't. *The first one has been done for you.*

**Example:**
**Jenny:** Where *were* you yesterday?
**Karen:** I *was* on a boat with Terry and Kim. The weather *was* beautiful and we caught some fish. The fish *weren't* (not) very big!

1 **Mary:** .............. you in the office when Jenny telephoned?
  **Sam:** No, I .............. (not) here. I .............. at home.

2 **Richard:** .............. you in Atlanta for the 1996 Olympic Games?
  **Donna:** No, we .............. (not). But we .............. in Barcelona for the 1992 games.

3 **Mandy:** Why .............. your bike in the kitchen yesterday?
  **James:** There .............. a lot of rain and the streets .............. wet. A kitchen is a good place for a bike when it rains!

4 **Phil:** Why .............. (not) the children at school yesterday?
  **Anne:** They are on holiday this week. Remember?

5 **Alan:** .............. there many people at the football yesterday?
  **Michael:** No, there .............. not many people there. It .............. very cold and the game .............. very boring. Many fans went home. After an hour there .............. more people playing than watching!

# UNIT 13   Past Simple 1: Positive
## I worked; They went

## FORM

**POSITIVE**

**1** Look at these sentences.

*In the 16th century, people **believed** the world was flat.*

*They **walked** to the fish market yesterday.*

*We **had** a wonderful holiday. We **flew** to Miami, **drove** down to Argentina and then **took** a boat back to London.*

These verbs are in the past simple.

**2** To form the past simple

**A** add *-ed* to the base verb

I / You / He / She / It / We / They      walked

*I **worked** in a restaurant many years ago.*

*It **rained** yesterday.*

**But:**

**B** for most verbs ending in *-e* just add *-d*

*I **telephoned** you ten times yesterday! Where were you?*

*She **lived** in India when she was a child.*

**C** For verbs ending in a vowel + a consonant (*rob, shop*), double the consonant then add *-ed*

*He **robbed** the bank.*

*They **shopped** for ten hours. It was a good day!*

**D** For verbs ending in a consonant + *-y* (*hurry, cry*) change *y* to *i* and add *-ed*

*I **hurried** to work.*

*The baby **cried** for thirty minutes.*

**E** Some verbs do not change.

*She **hit** the ball.*

*I **cut** down the tree.*

**F** There are many irregular verbs (*see* page 86)

get – got, find – found, break – broke, take – took, say – said

## USE

We use the past simple to say when something happened in the past. For this reason, we often use the past simple:

**1** with the word *yesterday*

**2** with phrases like *last week* and *three months ago*

**3** with dates and years of the past like *28th*

---

### 1   Write the past simple

*Write the past simple of these verbs. Look at the list of irregular verbs on page 86 if you need help.*

1   work     *worked*
2   play     ...............
3   talk     ...............
4   write     ...............
5   eat     ...............
6   finish     ...............
7   read     ...............
8   find     ...............
9   drink     ...............
10   want     ...............
11   speak     ...............
12   answer     ...............
13   run     ...............
14   drive     ...............
15   fly     ...............
16   cry     ...............
17   try     ...............
18   come     ...............
19   leave     ...............
20   talk     ...............

### 2   Complete the dialogue

*It's Monday morning. John and Claire arrived at work a few moments ago. Put the verbs in the box in the past simple and use them to complete the dialogue. The first one has been done for you.*

> build   cook   cycle   get   go   play   paint   read   run
> sing   sleep   swim   wash   watch   work   write

**John:**   What did you do this weekend?

**Claire:**   Well, on Saturday I **(1)** *played* tennis with my brother, **(2)** ............. lunch for my family, **(3)** ............. my kitchen red, **(4)** ............. in the river near my house, **(5)** ............. twelve shirts, **(6)** ............. for six hours on my computer and **(7)** ............. to a party with my husband.

On Sunday, I **(8)** ............. up at 6 a.m., **(9)**............. 20 km in the park, **(10)** ............. the newspapers, **(11)** ............. a little house for our dog in the garden, **(12)** ............. letters to all my friends, **(13)** ............. some songs with my children and **(14)** ............. 100 km on my new bike. And what did you do at the weekend?

**John:** Me? Oh I was really busy. On Saturday, I **(15)** .............. television for twelve hours and on Sunday I stayed in bed and **(16)** .............. . That's why I'm really tired today!

## 3 Match the parts

*Put the verbs in brackets in the past simple. Then match the parts. The first one has been done for you.*

## 4 Write the correct form of the verb

| | |
|---|---|
| 1 Christopher Columbus *(went)* | a) the first photograph in 1839. |
| 2 Leonardo Da Vinci (paint) | b) Coca Cola in 1886. |
| 3 Edward Daguerre (take) | c) a picture of an aeroplane in 1511. |
| 4 Mr Rolls and Mr Royce (build) | d) their first restaurant in 1954. |
| 5 Mike Powell (jump) | e) their first car in 1906. |
| 6 William Shakespeare (write) | f) the first radio message in 1895. |
| 7 Thomas Gales (invent) | g) his first play in 1590. |
| 8 Guglielmo Marconi (send) | h) 9 metres in Tokyo in 1996. |
| 9 McDonalds (open) | i) to America in 1492. |

*Write the correct past simple form of the verb.*
**Example:**
She *bought* (buy) her first car in 1995.

1 Last Saturday we .............. (lose) our house keys. Luckily our son is small, and he .............. (climb) through a window.
2 I have a penfriend in New Zealand. I .............. (write) to her yesterday.
3 I .............. (make) some chocolate biscuits this morning. Have one!
4 Sally .............. (play) tennis with Jenny yesterday. After the match, they .............. (drink) some fruit juice at a cafe and .............. (talk) about their friends.

Then Sally .............. (go) home, .............. (take) a shower, and .............. (go) to bed.
5 I'm sorry I'm late. I .............. (wait) an hour for the bus.
6 I .............. (buy) a new camera last month and I .............. (take) these photographs. What do you think?
7 We .............. (meet) Jonathan on holiday two years ago.
8 We .............. (send) him a postcard from Cairo, but he never .............. (receive) it.
9 On the plane to Turkey, Jackie .............. (read) a book and then .............. (watch) a film.
10 The film was boring and very long. It .............. (start) at 7.00 and .............. (finish) at 11.15. After two hours, I .............. (fall) asleep and I .............. (wake) up when the lights came on!

## 5

*Complete the story of Robert Scott by writing the correct form of the verb in brackets.*
Robert Falcon Scott (**1** – live) from 1868 to 1912. He (**2** – join) the navy at the age of fourteen. He was very good and the navy (**3** – promote) him quickly. In 1900, he (**4** – lead) an expedition to Antarctica. He (**5** – explore) the eastern part of the continent. The expedition (**6** – make) a lot of important, scientific discoveries and (**7** – return) to England in 1904.

He (**8** – marry) and (**9** – have) one son. His son Peter (**10** – study) natural history about birds and animals, when he (**11** – grow) up.

After his return to England, Scott (**12** – want) to go back to Antarctica. The Geographical Association (**13** – pay) for the new journey. Scott (**14** – find) four companions and in 1910 (**15** – go) back to Antarctica. He (**16** – plan) to be the first man to reach the South Pole. They (**17** – have) a lot of difficulties; and when they (**18** – arrive) at the Pole, they (**19** – see) the Norwegian flag. Another explorer, Roald Amundsen, (**20** – get) there first.

The return journey through Antarctica was very difficult. They (**21** – have) bad weather and (**22** – become) ill. All of them (**23** – die). Scott was the last to die on 29th March 1912. Some people (**24** – find) their bodies two weeks later.

# UNIT 14    Past Simple 2: Negative and Questions
## It didn't rain; Did it rain?

## FORM

Look at these sentences.
*I **didn't play** tennis yesterday.*
*They **didn't understand** the question.*
***Did** it **rain** last night?*
***Did** you **post** that letter for me?*
These are negative and question forms of the past simple.

### NEGATIVE
subject + *didn't* + base verb
I / He / She / It / We / You / They     didn't eat
*We **didn't fly** to the island. We went by ferry.*

### QUESTIONS
*Did* + subject + base verb

Did I / he / she / it / we / you / they    eat?
***Did** you **buy** a newspaper?*
Remember, all verbs after *did* and *didn't* are in the base form.

### SHORT ANSWERS
We often give a short answer *(Yes, I did / No, they didn't)* to a question that begins with *did*.
Yes, I / he / she / it / we / you / they   did
No, I / he / she / it / we / you / they    didn't
*Did McDonalds open their first restaurant in 1951?*
*No, they **didn't**.*
*Did Mike Powell jump 9 metres in Tokyo?*
*Yes, he **did**.*

## USE

We often put question words like *who, what, when* and *where* before a past simple question to ask for information.

*When did McDonalds open their first restaurant?*
*Where did Mike Powell jump 9 metres?*
**Note:**
*Who* has some special uses. *See Unit 23.*

---

### 1   Make the sentences negative

**Example:**
They played table tennis.
*They **didn't play** table tennis.*

1   I ate your apple.      .........................
2   I bought a new car.     .........................
3   She understood the question.  .........................
4   They went to Germany.   .........................
5   We watched television.   .........................
6   I liked the film.      .........................
7   He read the newspaper.   .........................
8   The bus stopped.     .........................
9   She telephoned me.    .........................
10   They knew the words of the song.  .........................
11   They drank coffee.    .........................
12   She found the money.   .........................
13   I lost my keys.      .........................
14   The dog ran away.    .........................
15   We played tennis.    .........................

### 2   Complete the sentences

*Complete the sentences. Use* didn't *and a verb from the box.*

| catch | comb | drink | eat | finish | play | put |
|-------|------|-------|-----|--------|------|-----|
| sleep | spend | rain | read | return | take | wear | win |

**Example:**
She wrote a letter but she *didn't post* it.

1   They made some sandwiches but they .......... them.
2   I took an umbrella but it .......... .
3   They bought a newspaper but they .......... it.
4   He made an orange juice but he .......... it.
5   He washed his hair but he .......... it.
6   I started the book but I .......... it.
7   He bought some new shoes but he .......... them.
8   She bought some records but she .......... them.
9   She went to the station but she .......... the train.
10   We found some money but we .......... it.
11   We played the football match but we .......... it.
12   She borrowed my coat but she .......... it.
13   He had a camera but he .......... any photographs.
14   They had ten bedrooms but they .......... in them.
15   I had some coffee but I ..... sugar in it.

## 3 Ask questions

*Your sister went to Italy on holiday last week. Ask questions about her trip.*
**Example:**
Ask her if she ate spaghetti.    *Did you eat spaghetti?*

1  Ask her if she went to the beach.          ................?
2  Ask her if she swam in the sea.            ................?
3  Ask her if she stayed in a nice hotel.     ................?
4  Ask her if she ate a lot of ice-cream.     ................?
5  Ask her if she met any interesting people ................?
6  Ask her if she went to Florence.           ................?
7  Ask her if she bought some Italian shoes ................?
8  Ask her if she sent any postcards.         ................?
9  Ask her if she drank a lot of coffee.      ................?
10 Ask her if she brought you a present.      ................?
11 Ask her if she sat in the sun.             ................?
12 Ask her if she went dancing.               ................?
13 Ask her if she read any books.             ................?
14 Ask her if she liked her holiday.          ................?
15 Ask her if she wanted to come home         ................?

## 4 Make questions

*Put the words in the right order to make questions.*
**Example:**
did / where / buy / you / that / dress
*Where did you buy that dress?*

1  where / last year / you / did / go on holiday
2  the train / did / at the station / when / arrive
3  you / how / did / get there
4  you / did / buy / 15 blue pencils / why
5  who / they / invite / did / to the party
6  when / Marconi / the first radio message / send / did
7  when / the first photograph / take / did / Daguerre
8  where / Columbus / did / in 1492 / go
9  did / what / Mr Rolls and Mr Royce / in 1906 / build
10 what time / the lesson / did / begin / yesterday
11 she / leave / did / when
12 painting / you / that / find / where / interesting / did
13 wife / your / become / a teacher / when / did
14 for / dinner / what / you / have / did
15 when / your house / you / did / buy

## 5 Make questions and answers

*Make past simple questions and short answers.*
**Examples:**
you / post that letter for me?
*Did you post that letter for me?*

Yes, *I did*. I went to the post office at about 3 o'clock.
they / go to the party last night?
*Did they go to the party last night?*
No, *they didn't*. They were very tired.

1  she / do the homework?
...................
   Yes, .......... . And she got all the answers right.
2  you / eat all the biscuits?
...................
   No, .......... . I ate five, maybe six.
3  they / meet you at the station?
...................
   No, .......... . I had to take a taxi.
4  he / buy a new car?
...................
   Yes, .......... . He bought a Volvo.
5  they / win the match?
...................
   No, .......... . They lost 4–3, but it was an exciting game.
6  he / make his bed this morning?
...................
   No, .......... . He's very untidy!
7  Jenny / make this bread?
...................
   Yes, .......... . It tastes delicious.
8  it / snow last month?
...................
   Yes, .......... . We had about 20 centimetres.
9  they / wash up last night?
...................
   Yes, .......... . Tim washed and Tina dried.
10 they / enjoy their holiday?
...................
   No, .......... . It rained every day!
11 she / buy a new coat?
...................
   No, .......... . It was too expensive.
12 you / find your dog?
...................
   Yes, .......... . It was in the park.
13 they / go to France?
...................
   No, .......... . They went to Italy.
14 he / like the film?
...................
   No, .......... . It was boring.
15 she / catch the train?
...................
   Yes, .......... . It left twenty minutes ago.

# UNIT 15 — Past Continuous
## I was talking

## FORM AND USE

Look at the sentences.

*I* **was** tal**king**.
It **wasn't** rai**ning**.
**Were** they wat**ching**?

This is the past continuous
We form the past continuous with *was / were* + the *-ing* form of the verb.

### POSITIVE

| | | |
|---|---|---|
| I / He / She / It | was | talking |
| You / We / They | were | talking |

**Note:**
We always use the long form, *was* or *were*.

### NEGATIVE

| | | |
|---|---|---|
| I / He / She / It | was not | talking |
| You / We / They | were not | talking |
| I / He / She / It | wasn't | talking |
| You / We / They | weren't | talking |

**Note:**
We can use the long form or the short form.

### QUESTIONS

| | | |
|---|---|---|
| Was | I / he / she / it | talking? |
| Were | you / we / they | talking? |

## USE

**1** We use this tense to talk about the past. Generally when you see a past continuous you know that
**A** two things happened in the past
**B** a long action was interrupted by a short action
Look at this example.
*This morning ...*
*At 9.37, Jane sat down in the bath.*
*At 9.43, the telephone rang.*
*At 9.53, Jane got out of the bath.*

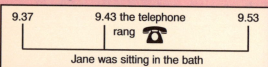

We can say
*The telephone* **rang**. *Jane* **was sitting** *in the bath.*
or

*Jane* **was sitting** *in the bath* **when** *the telephone* **rang**.
The long action (*Jane was sitting in the bath*) was interrupted by a short action (*the telephone rang*).

**2** You often see a past continuous and a past simple together. There are two common forms for this.
**A** past continuous + *when* + past simple
*Vivienne* **was studying** *at university* **when** *she* **met** *Jim.*
*They* **were walking** *in the forest* **when** *they* **saw** *an elephant!*
**B** the past simple before past continuous
*I* **woke up** *at three o'clock. It* **was snowing**.
*I* **saw** *Fred in the library yesterday. He* **was sleeping**!

**3** Remember that we often put words like *what* and *where* before a past continuous question.
**What were you doing** *when my letter arrived?*
**Where were you living** *when you met Harry?*

---

### 1 Write the correct form

*You went to a birthday party yesterday, but you arrived two hours early. Write the correct form of the verb to describe what you saw when you arrived at the house.*
**Example:**
Nick *was cleaning* (clean) his shoes.

1 Mark ............... (make) sandwiches in the kitchen.
2 Jennifer ............... (wash) the knives and forks.
3 Gerry and Tim ............... (put) cream on the birthday cake.
4 The dog ............... (sleep) by the fire.
5 Harry ............... (cook) potatoes.
6 Theresa ............... (put) the plates on the table.
7 Karen and Louisa ............... (buy) fruit juice at the supermarket.
8 Bob ............... (look) for his camera.
9 The baby ............... (cry).
10 Uncle Ted ............... (watch) TV and ............... (eat) chocolate.

### 2 Complete the sentences

*Complete the sentences with the correct form of the verb.*
**Example:**
I saw Sally yesterday. She *was waiting* (wait) for a bus.

1 I looked out the window. It ............... (rain).

2 I saw Naomi this afternoon. She ............... (go) to the post office.
3 I met Sam at the station. He ............... (wait) for the train to Geneva.
4 I saw a cat in a tree. It ............... (watch) a bird.
5 Tom was here. He ............... (look) for you.
6 I didn't answer the phone. I ............... (watch) a film on TV.
7 I met Alison at the supermarket. She ............... (buy) some fruit.
8 They closed the airport today. It ............... (snow).
9 I saw Richard this afternoon. He ............... (drive) a new car.
10 Tina was at the party. She ............... (wear) a green hat, a red shirt, a blue skirt and yellow shoes.

## 3 Write the correct form

*Write the correct form of the verb, past continuous or past simple.*

**Example:**

I *was swimming* (swim) in the river when I *saw* (see) a beautiful yellow fish.

1 Maria and Tim ............... (run) for the train when Maria ............... (fall).
2 I ............... (eat) a pizza in an Italian restaurant when the President of Bolivia ............... (come) in!
3 We ............... (play) golf when it ............... (start) to rain.
4 We ............... (drive) to Amsterdam when I ............... (ask) Karen to marry me.
5 He ............... (make) lunch when we ............... (ring).
6 It ............... (snow) when the plane ............... (arrive).
7 I ............... (live) in America when I ............... (see) my first basketball game.
8 We ............... (walk) to the shops when we ............... (meet) Gillian.
9 He ............... (listen) to the radio when he suddenly ............... (have) an idea.
10 It ............... (rain) when I ............... (go) to bed.

## 4 Complete the interview

*Twenty minutes ago, two people robbed a bank in Manchester High Street. A television reporter is interviewing people who saw what happened. Complete the interview, using the correct form of the past continuous. The first one has been done for you.*

**Reporter:** Mrs Preston, can I ask you the first question? Where (1) *were* you *standing* (stand) when the robbery happened.

**Mrs Preston:** I (2) ............... (stand) at the bus stop.

**Reporter:** What (3) ............... you ............... (do)?

**Mrs Preston:** I (4) ............... (wait) for a number 23 bus.

**Reporter:** Where (5) ............... you ............... (go)?

**Mrs Preston:** I (6) ............... (go) home, of course!

**Reporter:** What (7) ............... the first robber ............... (wear)?

**Mrs Preston:** He (8) ............... (wear) an orange T-shirt and jeans.

**Reporter:** What (9) ............... the first robber ............... (carry)?

**Mrs Preston?** He (10) ............... (carry) a gun!

**Reporter:** Thank you, Mrs Preston. Now, Mr Thompson, let me ask you some questions. Where (11) ............... you ............... (sit) when the robbery happened:

**Mr Thompson:** I (12) ............... (sit) in the Bluebird Café.

**Reporter:** What (13) ............... you ............... (do)?

**Mr Thompson:** I (14) ............... (drink) a cup of coffee.

**Reporter:** What (15) ............... the second robber ............... (wear)?

**Mr Thompson:** She (16) ............... (wear) a yellow dress.

**Reporter:** What (17) ............... the second robber ............... (carry)?

**Mr Thompson:** She (18) ............... (carry) a bag for the money.

**Reporter:** Thank you, Mr Thompson. Now, Mr Ford, can I ask you some questions? Where (19) ............... you ............... (work) when the robbery happened?

**Mr Ford:** I (20) ............... (work) in my ice-cream shop. I (21) ............... (make) chocolate ice-cream. We sell the best ice-cream in Manchester at our shop. It's just £3 a kilo! Our telephone number is ...

**Reporter:** Yes, thank you, Mr Ford!

# Present Perfect 1: Positive and Negative
## It has started; We haven't finished

## FORM

**1** Look at these sentences.
*I **have washed** my hair. It's still wet!*
*It **has started** to rain.*
*She **hasn't been** to Europe.*
*They **haven't seen** the film.*
These verbs are in the present perfect.

**2** We form the present perfect with *has / have* + the past participle. The past participle is formed by adding *-ed* to the base verb.
*wash – washed*
*finish – finished*

**3** Some verbs are irregular. *See page 86.*
**A** The past participle is sometimes the same as the past simple:
*buy – bought*
*find – found*
**B** The past participle is sometimes different from the past simple:

*go – went – gone*
*swim – swam – swum*

**POSITIVE**
**Long form**

| | |
|---|---|
| I / You / We / They | have started |
| He / She / It | has started |

**Short form**

| | |
|---|---|
| I've / You've / We've / They've | started |
| He's / She's / It's | started |

**NEGATIVE**
**Long form**

| | |
|---|---|
| I / You / We / They | have not started |
| He / She / It | has not started |

**Short form**

| | |
|---|---|
| I / You / We / They | haven't started |
| He / She / It | hasn't started |

**Note:**
The short form is much more common than the long form.

## USE

**1** We use the present perfect to talk about something in the past when
**A** we do not know, or we do not say when it happened
*She **has bought** a new car.*
(She still has the car, but we don't know, or we do not say when she bought it.)
**B** it still means something in the present
*They **have been** to India.*
(We do not know when they went to India, but it is still important for them.)

**2** We often put the word *just* before the past participle. In these sentences *just* means very, very recently.
*The train **has just arrived**. The station is full of people.*
*I've **just spoken** to Samantha. She's very excited about the holiday.*

**3** The participles *gone* and *been* have different meanings
**A** *he's gone* = he's not here, he's there
*Can I speak to Tim, please?*
*He's not here. **He's gone** to the grocer's to buy some tea.*
**B** *he's been* = he was there but now he's here
(an hour later) *Can I speak to Tim, please?*
*Yes, he's here now. **He's been** to the grocer's. We're drinking tea!*

**4** With the present perfect, we do not say when the event happened. If you say when something happened, you use the past simple.

| Present perfect | Past simple |
|---|---|
| *I've read your letter.* | *I read your letter **yesterday**.* |
| *I've made breakfast.* | *I made breakfast **three hours ago**.* |

---

**1** **Write positive sentences**

*Write positive sentences, using short forms of the present perfect.*
**Example:**
He / go / to the supermarket *He's gone to the supermarket.*

1 She / spend / all her money .....................
2 They / buy / a big house near the sea .....................

3 I / start / to / learn / English .....................
4 He / drink / ten cups of tea today! .....................
5 They / eat / all my chocolate! .....................
6 I / make / a few mistakes .....................
7 I / do / a lot of work today .....................
8 I / put / a hot-water bottle in the bed .....................
9 They / make / some toast .....................
10 She / take the dog for a walk .....................
11 He / miss the bus! .....................
12 She / lose her passport! .....................

## 2 Write negative sentences

*Write negative sentences, using short forms.*
**Example:**
I / not see / her new flat
*I haven't seen her new flat.*

1  She / not answer / my letter ...................
2  They / not read / all of the book ...................
3  He / not send / me the money ...................
4  We / not understand / this very well ...................
5  It / not rain / for two weeks ...................
6  We / not sing / this song for years ...................
7  They / not plan / their holiday ...................
8  She / not read / the newspaper ...................
9  I / not be / to Pakistan ...................
10 I / not climb / Mount Everest ...................
11 We / not paint / the bathroom ...................
12 The dog / not eat / its food ...................

## 3 Complete the dialogue

*You have just come home after a long day at the office. You want to make a cup of tea, relax and talk with Fred, your brother. Complete the dialogue using the past participles of the verbs in the box. The first one has been done for you.*

| ask | break | buy | drink | eat | sell |
|-----|-------|-----|-------|-----|------|

**You:** Where is my cup, Fred?
**Fred:** Erm ... I've (**1**) *broken* it. Sorry!
**You:** And Fred, where's my chocolate cake?
**Fred:** Erm ... I've (**2**) ............... it. Sorry!
**You:** And Fred, where's my milk?
**Fred:** Erm ... I've (**3**) ............... it. Sorry!
**You:** And Fred, where's my bicycle?
**Fred:** Erm ... I've (**4**) ............... it. Sorry!
**You:** You've sold my bicycle! And what have you done with the money?
**Fred:** Erm ... I've (**5**) ............... two tickets for the football tonight.
**You:** But you know that I don't like football, Fred ...
**Fred:** That's OK, because I've (**6**) ............... my girl-friend to go with me!

## 4 Complete the sentences

*Complete the sentences with* been *or* gone. *The first one has been done for you.*

1  Jenny's *been* to Singapore. It looks wonderful. She showed me the photographs last night.
2  They're not here at the moment. They've ............... to lunch.
3  I've ............... to the chemist's. I got your medicine.
4  He's ............... to Jamaica. He'll be back next week.
5  It's 3 a.m. The school is closed. Everyone has ............... home.
6  I've ............... to the shops, and we've got every thing for dinner tonight.
7  She's ............... to the cinema. I don't know when the film finishes.
8  We've ............... to Spain many times. We really like it there.
9  They've ............... to their parents. They see them every weekend.
10 She's ............... to work. You can phone her there.

## 5 Match the parts

*Match the parts of the sentences in A and B. Then write the sentences, using* just + *present perfect. The first one has been done for you.*

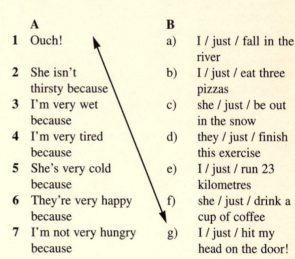

| | A | | B |
|---|---|---|---|
| 1 | Ouch! | a) | I / just / fall in the river |
| 2 | She isn't thirsty because | b) | I / just / eat three pizzas |
| 3 | I'm very wet because | c) | she / just / be out in the snow |
| 4 | I'm very tired because | d) | they / just / finish this exercise |
| 5 | She's very cold because | e) | I / just / run 23 kilometres |
| 6 | They're very happy because | f) | she / just / drink a cup of coffee |
| 7 | I'm not very hungry because | g) | I / just / hit my head on the door! |

1  *Ouch! I have just hit my head on the door!*

---

# UNIT 17  Present Perfect 2: Questions
## Have you ever been to Hong Kong?

## FORM

**1**  Look at these sentences.
*Has she been to Hong Kong?*
*Have you ever ridden a horse?*
*Have the children gone to school yet?*
These are question forms of the present perfect.

**2**  To make a question in the present perfect, we put *has* or *have* at the beginning of the sentence:
*has / have* + subject + past participle
Have I / you / we / they   finished?
Has he / she /it        finished?
*Has Tom arrived?*
*Have you seen my yellow socks?*
**Note:**
We always use the long form for questions.

**3**  We often use *has* or *have* in a short answer to a present perfect question.
*Have you seen my pen?*
*Yes, I have. / No, I haven't.*
*Has Jenny gone to lunch?*
*Yes, she has. / No, she hasn't.*
**Positive short forms**
Yes, I / you / we / they   have
Yes, he / she / it        has
**Negative short forms**
No, I / you / we / they   haven't
No, he / she / it        hasn't

## USE

**1**  Remember that we do not use the present perfect if we say when something happened (*see* Unit 16). We say *I saw the film yesterday.* (not *I have seen the film yesterday*.)
In the same way, when we ask a question with the present perfect we do not use the word *yesterday* or phrases like *last week, three months ago* or *in 1997*.
Compare the present perfect question
*Have you been to China?*
with the simple past question
*Did you go to China in 1997?*
**Present perfect + *ever***
**1**  To make a present perfect question stronger, we can add the word *ever* (at any time in your life).
*Have you ever eaten French food?*

**2**  We often use *never* (= at no time) when we give a negative answer.
*No, I've never eaten French food.*
(*See* Unit 36 for more about adverbs of frequency like *ever* and *never*.)
**Present perfect + *yet***
We also use *yet* (= already) in a present perfect question to make it stronger.
*Has the plane arrived yet?*
We often repeat the word *yet* when we give a negative answer.
*No, it hasn't arrived yet.*
**Note:**
We normally put *yet* at the end of a sentence.

---

**1**  **Make questions in the present perfect**

**Example:**
you / finish / your homework
*Have you finished your homework?*

1  Jackie / eat / all the biscuits   ....................?
2  you / read / this book   ....................?
3  you / see / my green pencil   ....................?
4  you / make / your bed   ....................?
5  she / open / the letter   ....................?
6  Jim / go / to the bank   ....................?
7  you / thank / her for the present   ....................?
8  you / clean / your shoes   ....................?
9  she / buy / a new piano   ....................?
10 he / wash / the car   ....................?

**2**  **Make questions**

*Make questions, using the present perfect and* ever.
**Example:**
you ever / be / on television?
*Have you ever been on television?*

1  you ever / work / in a restaurant?
2  you ever / take / a photograph of an elephant?
3  you ever / sleep / on a train?
4  you ever / wash / your shirt / in a river?
5  you ever / tell / a lie?
6  you ever / be / in a desert?

### 3 Make questions and answers

*You are a writer for a newspaper. You are interviewing James Promise, the famous film star. Make questions with* ever *and write short answers.*

**Example:**

you ever / be / in love
*Have you ever been in love?*
No, I *haven't*, but maybe I'll be lucky soon.

**1** you ever / drive / a Ferrari ....................?
   Yes, I ............. . I have two Ferraris and three Rolls-Royces.
**2** you ever / be / to Australia? ....................?
   Yes, I ............. . I'm famous there!
**3** you ever / write / a book ....................?
   No, I ............. , but many people have written books about me.
**4** you ever / write / a letter to a film star ....................?
   No, ............. , but many people write letters to me.
**5** you ever / give / a long interview ....................?
   No, I ............. . Thank you. Goodbye.

### 4 Write questions and answers

**Example:**

you / ever / be / to Bolivia?
No / I / never / be / to / Bolivia.
But / I / be / to Argentina.
*Have you ever been to Bolivia?*
*No, I've never been to Bolivia.*
*But I've been to Argentina.*

**1** you / ever / play cricket
   No / I / never / play / cricket.
   But / I / play / baseball.
**2** she / ever / eat / Indonesian food?
   No / she / never / eat / Indonesian food.
   But / she / eat Thai food.
**3** they / ever / meet / your brother?
   No / they / never / meet / my brother.
   But / they / meet / my sister.
**4** he / ever / be / on an aeroplane?
   No / he / never / be / on an aeroplane.
   But / he / be / in a helicopter.
**5** you / ever / swim / in the sea?
   No / I / never / swim / in the sea.
   But / I / swim / in a river.
**6** you / ever / drive / a train?
   No / I / never / drive a train.
   But / I / drive / a car.

### 5 Make questions and answers

*Make questions and give negative answers with the present perfect and* yet.

**Examples:**

you / finish / your homework / yet?
*Have you finished your homework yet?*
*No, I haven't finished my homework yet.*
she / take / the exam / yet?
*Has she taken the exam yet?*
*No, she hasn't taken the exam yet.*

**1** you / find / your yellow socks / yet?
**2** they / clean / the windows / yet?
**3** the train / arrive / yet?
**4** you / have / lunch / yet?
**5** you  / make / any mistakes / yet?
**6** she / read / the magazine / yet?
**7** you / finish / this exercise / yet?
**8** you / take / the dog for a walk / yet?

### 6 Put the words in the right order

*Put the words in sentences 1–7 in the right order to make a question. Then match these questions with the right answers, a–g.*

**1** have / you / the Amazon / seen / ever?
**2** Francesca / to Milan / gone / has / by plane?
**3** my newspaper / seen / you / have?
**4** have / the dog / given / you / its / food?
**5** your hair / you / washed / have?
**6** have / new shoes / some / bought / you?
**7** dinner / yet / you / had / have?

**a** Yes, it's in the bedroom.
**b** Yes, and then I took it for a walk in the park.
**c** No, I've cleaned my old ones!
**d** No. Shall we go to a restaurant?
**e** No, she hates flying so she's gone there by train.
**f** No, I was waiting by the bus stop and it was raining!
**g** Yes, we went to Brazil last year.

# UNIT 18  The Future 1: *be going to*
## It's going to snow

## FORM

Look at these sentences.
*I am going to buy some new shoes tomorrow.*
*He is going to be rich one day.*
*Are they going to pass the exam?*
We form this future tense with the verb *to be* (*am / is / are*) + *going to* + base verb.

### POSITIVE
We can use a long form

| I | am | going to | eat |
|---|---|---|---|
| He / She / It | is | going to | eat |
| You / We / They | are | going to | eat |

or a short form

| I'm | | going to | eat |
|---|---|---|---|
| He's / She's / It's | | going to | eat |
| You're / We're / They're | | going to | eat |

*He's going to win!*
*You are going to study hard this year.*

### NEGATIVE
We make the verb *to be* negative, then add *going to* + base verb.

| I | am | not | going to | eat |
|---|---|---|---|---|
| He / She / It is | | not | going to | eat |

| You / We / They | are | not | going to | eat |

There are two short forms

| I'm | not going to | eat |
|---|---|---|
| He's / She's / It's | not going to | eat |
| We're / You're / They're | not going to | eat |

or

| He / She / It | isn't going to | eat |
|---|---|---|
| We / You / They | aren't going to | eat |

**Note:**
There is only one short form for first person singular *(I)*. We say
*I'm not going to eat.* (not *I amn't going to eat* ).

### QUESTIONS
To make a question, we put the verb *to be* before the subject.

| Am | I | going to | eat? |
|---|---|---|---|
| Is | he / she / it | going to | eat? |
| Are | we / you / they | going to | eat? |

When we talk about more than one thing in the future, it is not necessary to repeat *be going to*.
*I'm going to have a shower and go to bed.*
*She's going to wake up early and run in the park.*

## USE

We use *be going to* + base verb to talk about
**1** our plans for the future
*I'm going to be a doctor.*
*They're going to buy a new house next year.*
**2** what is going to happen soon
*It's very cold today. I think it's going to snow.*
*I'm hungry. I'm going to eat some biscuits.*

**Note:**
We don't often use *going to go* or *going to come*. Instead we use the present continuous form of *go* or *come*.
*I'm going to Paris next week.*
*He's coming to see me on Tuesday.*

### 1  Complete the sentences

*Complete the sentences. Use the short form of* be going to.
**Example:**
It's my birthday. We*'re going to* have a party tonight.

1  I'm tired. I ............... sleep for half an hour.
2  She's hungry. She ............... have some fruit.
3  They're thirsty. They ............... drink some water.
4  I'm hot. I ............... open the window.
5  I'm cold. I ............... close the window.
6  He's bored. He ............... find a new job.
7  We're late. We ............... run to the station.

8  She loves films. She ............... go to the cinema tonight.
9  She's sad. She ............... to phone her friends.
10  He's got a new job. He ............... arrive at work early.
11  We're on holiday. We're ............... lie on the beach.
12  He wants more money. He ............... work all the time.
13  I'm rich now. I'm ............... buy a new house.
14  We haven't got any food in the house. We're ............... eat at a restaurant.
15  She studies a lot. She ............... pass her exams.

## 2 Write sentences

*You are on holiday. The tour guide has planned everything. This is what you are going to do. Write sentences about your week.*

**Example:**

Sunday: visit a museum / take some photographs
*On Sunday, we're going to visit a museum and take some photographs.*

1  Monday: play tennis / swim
   .............. we're .............. and .............. .
2  Tuesday: eat fish and chips / see a film
   .............. we're .............. and .............. .
3  Wednesday: walk to the mountains / have a picnic
   .............. we're .............. and .............. .
4  Thursday: walk in the countryside / ride a horse
   .............. we're .............. and .............. .
5  Friday: take a boat / visit some islands
   .............. we're .............. and .............. .
6  Saturday: take a taxi to the airport / fly home
   .............. we're .............. and .............. .

## 3 Complete the sentences

*Complete the sentences. Use the short negative forms of* to be going to.

**Examples:**

I*'m not going to* watch TV. I'm going to read a book.
She *isn't going to* learn Chinese. She's going to learn Japanese.

1  We .............. cook dinner tonight. We're going to eat at a restaurant.
2  We .............. stay on the beach. I think it's going to rain.
3  He .............. listen to records. He's going to listen to the radio.
4  They .............. by bus. They're going to travel by car.
5  She .............. wear a dress today. She's going to wear trousers.
6  It .............. rain today. You don't need an umbrella.
7  I .............. run for the bus. I'm going to wait for the next one.
8  He .............. buy a typewriter. He's going to buy a computer.
9  She .............. marry you. She's going to marry me.
10  They .............. work today. It's Sunday.

## 4 Make questions

**Examples:**

you / play / tennis tomorrow?
*Are you going to play tennis tomorrow?*
they / buy a new flat?
*Are they going to buy a new flat?*

1  they / buy a dog?
2  you / eat all that pizza?
3  he / play golf at the weekend?
4  you / have a holiday this year?
5  it / snow tomorrow?
6  you / tell me the truth?
7  he / win the game?
8  you / wash the dishes?
9  you / build a snowman this year?
10  they / sing that song again?

## 5 Complete the dialogue

*Sarah has gone to see Madame Futuro (MF) about her future with her boyfriend, Tim. Complete the dialogue using the* be going to *future. The first two have been done for you.*

**Sarah:** (1) *Am I going to* be a teacher?
**MF:** Yes. You (2) *'re going to* teach English!
**Sarah:** (3) .............. I .............. marry my boyfriend, Tim?
**MF:** Yes. And you (4) .............. have nine children!
**Sarah:** (5) .............. we .............. live in the city?
**MF:** No. You (6) .............. live in the countryside.
**Sarah:** (7) .............. we .............. live in a flat?
**MF:** No. You (8) .............. live in a big house.
**Sarah:** (9) .............. we .............. have a garden?
**MF:** Yes. You (10) .............. have a beautiful garden with lots of trees.
**Sarah:** (11) .............. we .............. have lots of pets?
**MF:** Yes. You (12) .............. have three dogs, two cats and a parrot!
**Sarah:** (13) .............. we have lots of holidays?
**MF:** Yes. You (14) .............. travel all over the world.
**Sarah:** (15) .............. we .............. be happy?
**MF:** Yes. You (16) .............. be very happy.
**Sarah:** (17) .............. we .............. be rich?
**MF:** Perhaps. But first you (18) .............. pay me £100. Thank you.

## UNIT 19  The Future 2: *will / shall*
### I'll see you next week

## FORM

*Look at these sentences.*
**I'll see** *you next week.*
**The sun will rise** *at 6.30 tomorrow.*
**Will the train arrive** *at 3.30 or 4 o'clock?*
**Shall** *we* **dance**?
These verbs are in the future simple.

**POSITIVE**
We use subject + *will* (*'ll*) + base verb for a positive sentence.
I / He / She / It / We / You / They      will have dinner tonight
**They will take** *an exam next month.*
**I'll call** *you tomorrow.*

**NEGATIVE**
We use subject + *will not* (*won't*) + base verb for a negative sentence.
I / He / She / It / We / You / They      will not have dinner tonight
*£30.00 for a pizza! We* **will not go** *to that restaurant again!*
*I* **won't go** *to work today. I'll stay in bed and sleep.*

**QUESTIONS**
We use *will / shall* + subject + base verb for questions.
Will I / he / she / it / we / you / they      have dinner tonight?
Shall  I / we have dinner tonight?
**Will you buy** *a new computer next year?*
**Shall I open** *the window? It's very hot in here.*

## USE

**1**  We use the future simple with *will* to talk about
**A**  things we know will happen in the future.
*It's my birthday tomorrow. I'll be 22 years old.*
**B**  things we think will happen in the future
*I'll be famous one day!*
**Notes:**
**A**  We normally use the short form *'ll* in conversation. We normally use the short form *won't* in conversation and in writing.
**B**  We can use *shall* for statements (*I shall be there tomorrow*) but we normally use *will*.
**2**  For questions we use
**A**  *Will* + base verb to ask for information
**Will** *the film* **start** *at 8 or 8.30?*

**B**  *Shall I* + base verb to make an offer
*You look hungry.* **Shall I make** *you a sandwich?*
[*Shall I* = I can do this if you like.]
**C**  *Shall we* + base verb for a suggestion
*It's raining!* **Shall we** *take a taxi?*
[*Shall we* = We can do this if you like.]
**Note:**
We only use *shall* with *I* and *we*.
**3**  We often put words like *what, when, where* and *who* before questions with *will*.
**What** *will you do tomorrow?*
**When** *will I see you again?*

---

### 1  Complete the sentences

*David works in a restaurant. He doesn't like his job. He dreams about the future. Complete the sentences with* I'll *or* I won't.
**Examples:**
I'll be rich one day. And then ...
*I won't* stand at the bus stop for 20 minutes every day!
*I'll* buy a new car. A Ferrari is nice!

1  .......... buy a big house near the sea.
2  .......... buy my own aeroplane.
3  .......... fly around the world.
4  .......... visit the Taj Mahal and take lots of photographs.
5  .......... work in this noisy restaurant.
6  .......... wash up all these dishes.
7  .......... cook food for the customers. I don't like them!
8  .......... go to the cinema every day. I love films.
9  .......... buy 150 pairs of shoes.
10  .......... buy a new television for my best friend, Tim.
11  .......... work until 11 o'clock every night.
12  .......... eat in restaurants, not work in them.

## 2 Complete the sentences

*Complete the sentences about the future. Use* will *and a verb from the box. The first one has been done for you.*

| | | | | | |
|---|---|---|---|---|---|
| be | die | drink | drive | eat | fly |
| live | speak | spend | wear | work | use |

1 One day people *will live* in cities on the moon.
2 Everybody .......... three meals a day.
3 There .......... a computer in every home.
4 Nobody .......... . Computers will do everything.
5 Aeroplanes .......... at 2,000 km an hour.
6 Everyone .......... the same language.
7 Everybody .......... clean water.
8 Everybody .......... trousers!
9 Nobody .......... money. Everything will be free.
10 People .......... small cars.
11 These cars .......... electricity.
12 Nobody .......... of hunger.

*Do you agree with these ideas? Will the future be like this? Write five sentences about things that* you *think will happen in the future.*

## 3 Write the dialogue

*You are going on holiday. The travel agent is answering your questions. Write the dialogue, using* will. *The first one has been done for you.*

1 When / the holiday start?
   *When will the holiday start?*
   The holiday / start on 1st June
   *The holiday will start on 1st June.*
2 When / the holiday end?
   The holiday / end on June 11th
3 What / the temperature be at that time of year?
   The temperature / be about 25˚C
4 Where / we stay?
   You / stay in a five star hotel
5 How / we get there?
   You / fly there from Manchester Airport
6 How long / the flight be?
   The flight / be four hours
7 How / we get from the airport to the hotel?
   You / get to the hotel by taxi
8 Where / we have breakfast?
   You / have breakfast in the hotel dining room
9 Where / we have lunch?
   You / have lunch on the beach!
10 Where / we have dinner?
   You / have dinner in one of the local restaurants
11 What / we do there?
   You / sit in the sun, swim and eat
12 How much / the holiday cost?
   It / cost £500 per person

## 4 Complete the sentences

*Complete the sentences, using* will *or* shall.
**Examples:**
*Will* they play tennis tomorrow?
*Shall* we take a taxi?

1 .......... we dance?
2 .......... I help you with those books? They look heavy!
3 .......... I make you some tea? You look thirsty.
4 .......... I make you some breakfast? You look hungry.
5 .......... you eat that cake, or can I have it?
6 .......... we listen to the radio?
7 .......... the plane arrive today or tomorrow?
8 .......... you marry me?
9 .......... February have 28 days or 29 days this year?
10 .......... you wake me up at 7.00 tomorrow, please?
11 .......... I buy a ticket for the cinema or the theatre?
12 .......... we go now? It's very late.

## 5 Complete the dialogues

*Complete these conversations. Use* Shall I *or* Shall we.

1 **Jim:** I'm tired. I don't want to go out tonight.
   **Vivienne:** *Shall we* stay at home and watch TV?
2 **Peter:** The weather's beautiful and I'm not working today.
   **Jane:** .......... go to the beach?
3 **Tim:** I've got a headache!
   **Michael:** I'm going to the chemist's. .......... get you some aspirin?
4 **Ian:** This bag is very heavy!
   **Diana:** .......... carry it for you.
5 **Bill:** I think we've missed the bus.
   **Jane:** .......... take a taxi or .......... walk?
   **Bill:** Let's walk. We don't have much money.
6 **Jenny:** I don't understand the difference between 'shall I' and 'shall we'.
   **Harriet:** .......... explain it again or .......... stop work and go and have a pizza?

# UNIT 20　Modals 1: *must / have to*

## FORM

<table>
<tr><td>

**1** Look at these sentences.<br>
*You **must do** your homework tonight.*<br>
*You **have to pay** for food in a restaurant.*<br>
*You **mustn't go** near that dog. It's dangerous!*<br>
*You **don't have to** go to work tomorrow. It's Sunday.*

| | |
|---|---|
| *must / have to* | = an obligation. |
| *mustn't* | = don't do it! It's dangerous, not allowed, or wrong! |
| *don't have to* | = it is not necessary; you decide. |

**2** We always use the base verb after *must* and *has / have / had to*.

subject + *must* + base verb<br>
subject + *mustn't* + base verb<br>
subject + *has / have / had to* + base verb<br>
subject + *doesn't / don't / didn't* + *have to* + base verb<br>
*Must* + subject + base verb?<br>
*Do / does / did* + subject + have to + base verb?

**POSITIVE**

| | | |
|---|---|---|
| I / You / He / She / It / We / You / They | must | eat |

*You must drive on the right in America.*

</td><td>

| | | |
|---|---|---|
| I / You / We / They | have to | eat |
| He / She / It | has to | eat |

*You have to drive on the right in America.*

**NEGATIVE**

| | | |
|---|---|---|
| I / He / She / It / We / You /They | must not (mustn't) | eat |

*You must not smoke here.*

We normally use the short form *(mustn't)* in conversation and in writing.

| | | |
|---|---|---|
| I / You / We / They | don't have to | eat |
| He / She / It | doesn't have to | eat |

*You don't have to pay now.*

**QUESTIONS**

| | | |
|---|---|---|
| Must | I / you / he / she / it / we / you / they | eat this? |

or

**Present**

| | | |
|---|---|---|
| Do | I / you / we / they | have to | eat? |
| Does | he / she / it | have to | eat? |

**Past**

| | | |
|---|---|---|
| Did | I / he / she / it / we / you / they | have to | eat? |

</td></tr>
</table>

## USE

**1** We use *must, must not (mustn't), has to* and *have to* to talk about the present or the future.

*I **must work** hard today. I have an exam tomorrow.*<br>
*I can't come to the cinema tonight. I **have to work**.*

**2** We do not use *must* to talk about the past. We use *had to* and *didn't have to*.

*I **had to study** hard **yesterday**. I had a lot of homework.*<br>
*They **didn't have to work yesterday**. It was Sunday.*

---

**1** **Complete the sentences**

*Complete the sentences. Use* must *or* mustn't.<br>
**Examples:**<br>
You *must* buy a ticket before you go on the train.<br>
You *mustn't* go on the train without a ticket!

1 You .......... eat vegetables and fruit. They're good for you.
2 You .......... eat fast food every day. It's bad for you.
3 You .......... take money from my bag?
4 We don't have any sugar. We .......... buy some today.
5 In Britain we drive on the left. You .......... drive on the right.
6 In Sweden they drive on the right. You .......... drive on the right. You .......... drive on the left.
7 You .......... take your medicine three times a day.

8 We don't have much petrol. We .......... find a petrol station.
9 You were in the garden. You ..........wash your hands before lunch.
10 You .......... tell a lie. You .......... always tell the truth.
11 This is my birthday party. We .......... talk about English grammar!
12 Uncle James is coming to dinner. We .......... clean the flat.

**2** **Complete the sentences**

*Complete the sentences. Use* has to, have to *or* had to.<br>
**Example:**<br>
Is that the time? I *have to* go!

1 She doesn't have a car. She .......... take the bus to work.

2 We're going to America tomorrow. We'll ......... buy some dollars today.

3 The plane leaves at 6. We ......... be at the airport by 4.30.

4 I had toothache yesterday. I ......... go to the dentist.

5 They missed the last bus. They ......... take a taxi home.

6 Fred has an elephant. He ......... buy a lot of bananas.

7 I'm sorry I'm late. I ......... wait two hours for a train!

8 I want to be a doctor. I'll ......... study medicine for seven years.

9 We went to a very expensive restaurant yesterday. I ......... wear a tie!

10 He ......... go to the post office. He needed some stamps.

11 He's a doorman. He ......... work in the rain, in the sun and in the snow.

12 The train leaves in twenty minutes. Come on! We ......... go.

## 3   Make questions

*Make questions, using* have to *in present or past.*
**Examples:**
I / go to school today?
*Do I have to go to school today?*
She / walk home last night?
*Did she have to walk home last night?*

1 we / answer / every question in the exam?
2 he / work on Saturdays?
3 she / wear glasses to read?
4 you / pay to go to the doctor's. Or is it free?
5 we / pay to use the library? Or is it free?
6 you / wear a uniform at your school? Or can you wear jeans?
7 you / do homework last night?
8 you / use a dictionary? Or did you know all the words?
9 they / buy a map? Or did they know the way?
10 you / use a key? Or was the door open?

## 4   Make questions

*Put the underlined words in the right order to make questions.*
**Example:**
go / must / you? It's only 9 o'clock.
*Must you go? It's only 9 o'clock.*

1 you / on the left or the right/ drive / must / in Australia?
2 I'm going to Canada. a visa / get / I / must?
3 we / go by boat / must? Or can we fly to the island?
4 I'm tired. go to the party / we / must?
5 I hate vegetables! all these carrots / eat / I / must?

## 5   Make negative sentences

*Make negative sentences in present or past.*
**Example:**
You / not / pay to go in the museum. It's free.
*You don't have to pay to go in the museum. It's free.*

1 She / not / work. She's very rich.
2 He / not / buy apples. There are ten apple trees in his garden.
3 You / not / shout! I can hear you.
4 You / not / wear a tie here. This is a fast food restaurant.
5 I / not / go to the office yesterday. It was Sunday.
6 I / not / buy a ticket for the concert yesterday. It was free.
7 They / not / take an umbrella yesterday. It wasn't raining.
8 This is a hotel and we're on holiday! You / not / make the beds today. You / not / wash the dishes today. You / not / clean the floors today. You / not / tidy the room today. You / not / cook three meals today. Let's go to the beach!

## 6   Complete the sentences

*Complete the sentences. Use* mustn't *or* don't have to.
**Examples:**
You *don't have to* go to work today. You're on holiday!
You *mustn't* drive fast! It's dangerous.

1 You ......... steal! It's wrong.
2 You ......... pay to go into this museum. It's free.
3 Shh! Please be quiet! You ......... talk in the library.
4 You ......... eat in the classroom. Take your sandwiches outside.
5 You ......... answer any more questions. You've done the exercise.

**Modals 2:** *can*
He can sing

## FORM

**1  Look at these sentences.**
*I* **can ride** *a bicycle but I* **can't drive** *a car.*
*These bags are very heavy.* **Can you help** *me?*
*Help her! She* **can't swim!**
We always use the base verb after *can*.
**POSITIVE**
I / He / She / It / We / You / They      can   swim
**NEGATIVE**
I / He / She / It / We / You / They      cannot (can't)
swim
**QUESTIONS**
Can I / he / she / it / we / you / they    swim?

**Short answers**
We often give a short answer to a question with *can*.
*Can you remember my name?*
*Yes, I can. / No, I can't.*
*Can he play the violin?*
*Yes, he can / No, he can't.*
**Positive**
Yes,  I / you / he / she / it / we / you / they   can
**Negative**
No,   I / you / he / she / it / we / you / they   can't

## USE

**1**  We use *can* to talk about what we are able to do.
*I'm from Tokyo. I* **can** *speak Japanese. It is an easy
language.*
*Birds* **can** *fly.*
*Carol and Tom* **can** *cook really well. They always eat at
home.*
**2**  We use *cannot (can't)* to talk about what we are not
able to do.
*I'm from London. I* **can't** *speak Japanese. It is a very
difficult language.*

*Elephants* **can't** *fly.*
*Mike and Jenny* **can't** *cook. They always eat in
restaurants.*
**Note:**
We use the short form *can't* more than the long form
*cannot* when we speak and when we write. *Cannot* is
very strong. We normally use this word when we are
angry. A mother says to her child: *You cannot watch the
film. Go to bed. Now!*

**1  Make sentences with** *can* **and** *can't*

**Examples:**
He / play the piano / not play the guitar
*He* **can** *play the piano but he* **can't** *play the guitar.*
He / speak Italian / not speak Portuguese.
*He* **can** *speak Italian but he* **can't** *speak Portuguese.*
1  She / play basketball / not play golf.
2  He / ride a bike / not drive a car.
3  My brother / remember faces / not remember
   names.
4  Her uncle / play the violin / not play the piano.
5  My sister / swim / not dance.
6  Her husband / dance / not swim.
7  I / make toast / not cook spaghetti.
8  My aunt / speak Turkish / not speak Russian.
9  Julia / sing / not paint.
10  Andrew / use a typewriter / not use a computer.
11  I / walk / not run.
12  My wife / swim / not drive.
13  Her dog / catch a ball / not catch a stick.
14  He / work in the day / not work at night.
15  Her sister / sing in private / not sing in public.

**2  Make questions**

*Put the words in the right order to make questions.*
**Example:**
dance / you / can                    *Can you dance?*
1   he / play / tennis / can             ...............?
2   swim / you / can                  ...............?
3   bread / can / make / you          ...............?
4   ride a bicycle / can your uncle     ...............?
5   can / a computer / use / you        ...............?
6   work / at night / can / you          ...............?
7   this question / you understand / can  ...............?
8   ride / a horse / you / can            ...............?
9   people in your country / cook well /
    can                               ...............?
10  drink tea / can / without sugar / you  ...............?
11  she / Spanish / speak / can          ...............?
12  music / can / you / read             ...............?
13  too / your brother / spaghetti / can /
    make                               ...............?
14  sleep / in the day / he / can          ...............?
15  they both / can / play / the violin      ...............?

# Answers

## UNIT 1

### Exercise 1
1 we're 2 he's 3 they're 4 she's
5 you're

### Exercise 2
1 we aren't 2 he isn't 3 they aren't
4 she isn't 5 you aren't

### Exercise 3
1 is 2 am 3 is 4 are 5 is 6 is 7 is 8 am,
is, is 9 are 10 is 11 is 12 are 13 are
14 am 15 is, am

### Exercise 4
1 'm 2 's 3 's 4 's 5 're 6 's 7 'm 8 's
9 're, 'm, 'm 10 're 11 's 12 's,'s 13 're
14 're 15 's

### Exercise 5
1 am not 2 is not 3 is not 4 is not 5 is
not 6 are not 7 is not 8 are not 9 is not
10 is not 11 is not 12 is not 13 are not
14 is not 15 am not

### Exercise 6
1 'm not 2 isn't 3 isn't 4 aren't 5
aren't 6 isn't 7 isn't 8 isn't 9 isn't 10
isn't 11 isn't 12 aren't 13 isn't 14 'm
not 15 isn't

## UNIT 2

### Exercise 1
1 Are 2 Is 3 Is 4 Is 5 Are 6 Are 7 Is
8 Am 9 Is 10 Are 11 Is 12 Are 13 Am
14 Is 15 Are

### Exercise 2
1 Are you ready?
2 Are you well?
3 Is your garden big?
4 Are these shoes expensive?
5 Is this answer right?
6 Are you thirsty?
7 Are your neighbours friendly?
8 Is the airport open?
9 Is this important?
10 Are these vegetables fresh?
11 Is that coffee hot?
12 Am I early?
13 Are we rich now?
14 Is he angry with me?
15 Is your car American?

### Exercise 3
1 Is it Spanish?
2 Am I right?
3 Is it Italian?
4 Is it 9 or 10?
5 Is he rich?
6 Is she hungry?
7 Are they fresh?
8 Is he wrong?
9 Is the taxi here?
10 Is it in the garden?
11 Are you ready?
12 Is it expensive?
13 Are we safe in it?
14 Is it in the Indian Ocean?
15 Is she Japanese?

### Exercise 4
1 Are, Yes, they are.
2 Is, No it isn't.
3 Is, No it isn't.
4 Is, Yes, she is.

5 Are, Yes, they are.
6 Are, Yes, they are.
7 Is, No it isn't.
8 Is, No it isn't.
9 Are, Yes, they are.
10 Is, No it isn't.
11 Is, Yes, he is.
12 Are, No, I'm not.
13 Are, No, they aren't.
14 Is, Yes, it is.
15 Are, No, we're not.

### Exercise 5:
1 (g) Is 2 (h) Am 3 (d) Is 4 (c) Is 5 (j)
Is 6 (k) Is 7 (b) Are 8 (e) Is 9 (f) Are
10 (a) Is 11 (i) Are

## UNIT 3

### Exercise 1
1 has 2 have 3 has 4 has 5 has 6 have
7 have 8 have 9 has 10 have 11 have
12 have 13 has 14 have 15 has

### Exercise 2
1 They don't have a cat.
2 She doesn't have red hair.
3 He doesn't have an expensive
watch.
4 I don't have a Japanese camera.
5 She doesn't have a bath every
day.
6 They don't have lunch at 12.30
7 He doesn't have a headache.
8 They don't have a garden.
9 We don't have a computer at
home.
10 I don't have a penfriend in New
Zealand.
11 She doesn't have a very good job.
12 We don't have three children.
13 They don't have a big house.
14 I don't have a brother.
15 We don't have a dog.

### Exercise 3
1 The fridge is empty. We don't
have any food.
2 I don't like animals. We don't
have any pets.
3 I'm on holiday. I don't have any
homework.
4 We're in a hurry. We don't have
any time.
5 You can't have toast. We don't
have any bread.
6 It's a very small village. It doesn't
have any shops.
7 She's unhappy. She doesn't have
a good job.
8 He's always angry. He doesn't
have any friends.
9 I don't like this coffee. It doesn't
have any sugar in it.
10 She's at the shops. She doesn't
have any bread or milk.

### Exercise 4
1 Do you have a headache?
2 Does he have an interesting job?
3 Do they have a garden?
4 Does she have short hair?
5 Do you have lunch at home?
6 Does he have a motorbike?
7 Do we have food in the fridge?

8 Do they have a holiday every
year?
9 Do you have a pen?
10 Do you have a penfriend in
Australia?

### Exercise 5
1 **Tina:** Do you have any brothers
or sisters?
**Philip:** I have three brothers but I
don't have any sisters.
2 **Sam:** Do you have any pets?
**Mary:** We have 15 dogs, 7 cats
and a parrot.
**Sam:** Do you have a holiday
every year?
**Mary:** A holiday? With 23
animals in the house! No,
we don't have any
holidays!
3 **Oliver:** Do you have tea with
your breakfast?
**Laura:** We don't have tea or
coffee. We only drink
fruit juice in the morning.
4 **Gina:** Is Tim OK?
**Tessa:** Not really. He has a
headache and he has a
cold.
**Gina:** I'm not surprised! It's the
middle of winter. It's -3°C.
There's 50 centimetres of
snow. But every morning
he has a swim in the river
and then walks home in
his T-shirt!

## UNIT 4

### Exercise 1
1 has got 2 has got 3 has got
4 have got 5 have got 6 has got
7 has got 8 have got 9 have got
10 has got

### Exercise 2
1 She hasn't got a dog.
2 I haven't got an Italian car.
3 We haven't got a computer in our
office.
4 He hasn't got white hair.
5 She hasn't got a headache.
6 They haven't got a garden.
7 I haven't got a penfriend in
Australia.
8 We haven't got a swimming pool
at our school.
9 She hasn't got a radio in her car.
10 We haven't got a cinema in our
village.

### Exercise 3
1 I can't drive you to the station. I
haven't got a car.
2 He can't go to Brazil. He hasn't
got a passport.
3 You can't go to the concert. You
haven't got a ticket.
4 It's a very small village. It hasn't
got a post office.
5 We can't phone her. We haven't
got her number.
6 They can't post the letter. They
haven't got a stamp.

### Exercise 4
1 Have you got a cold?
2 Has she got a good job?
3 Have they got a big garden?
4 Has she got long hair?
5 Has she got a bicycle?
6 Have we got any milk in the
fridge?
7 Have they got many friends?
8 Has she got a pen?
9 Have you got a question?
10 Have you got the answer?

### Exercise 5
2 has got 3 has got 4 haven't got
5 have got 6 have got 7 haven't got
8 has got 9 have got 10 haven't got
11 has got 12 have got 13 has got
14 have got 15 have got 16 haven't
got 17 haven't got 18 has got 19 has
got 20 has got 21 has got 22 have got
23 hasn't got 24 hasn't got 25 has got
Mrs Saunder's idea is very simple. Mr
Taylor brings his dog to the café and
Francesca takes the dog to the park.
Then Mr Taylor's friends come to the
café. The dog is not there so they are
not afraid. They all drink coffee
together and talk. The café is full. Mr
and Mrs Saunders sell a lot of coffee.
Mr Taylor sees all his friends. They
see him. And for a few hours, in the
park, Francesca has a dog.

## UNIT 5

### Exercise 1
1 There's a 2 There's a 3 There are
4 There are 5 There are 6 There's a
7 There are 8 There's a

### Exercise 2
1 There are 2 There are 3 There are
4 There's an 5 There are 6 There's a
7 There are 8 There's a 9 There's an
10 There's an

### Exercise 3
1 Is there 2 Are there 3 Is there
4 Is there 5 Is there 6 Is there
7 Are there 8 Are there 9 Are there
10 Is there

### Exercise 4
1 Are there, Yes, there are.
2 Are there, No, there aren't.
3 Are there, No there aren't.
4 Is there, No, there isn't.
5 Are there, Yes, there are.
6 Are there, No, there aren't.
7 Is there, No there isn't.
8 Are there, Yes, there are.
9 Are there, No, there aren't.
10 Is there, No, there isn't.
11 Are there, No there aren't.
12 Is there, No, there isn't.

### Exercise 5
1 There isn't any 2 There aren't any
3 There isn't any 4 There aren't any
5 There aren't any 6 There aren't any
7 There aren't any 8 There isn't any
9 There aren't any 10 There aren't
any

### Exercise 6
1 there are 2 There are 3 There are

4 there are 5 there aren't 6 a book
7 there are 8 there are 9 there is
10 there are 11 there are 12 there are
13 There is 14 a house 15 there are
16 There are 17 There are 18 There
are 19 there are 20 there are 21 cows

## UNIT 6
### Exercise 1
1 -s 2 -s 3 -s 4 -es 5 -s 6 -s 7 -s, -s
8 -es 9 -es 10 -s, -es 11 -s 12 -s, -s, -s
### Exercise 2
1 (d) goes 2 (e) teaches 3 (f) paints 4
(a) types 5 (b) looks 6 (c) works 7 (h)
cooks 8 (g) works
### Exercise 3
2 have 3 eat 4 drink 5 brush 6 put
7 leave 8 arrive 9 look 10 read
11 sleep 12 write 13 telephone
14 lives 15 talk 16 are 17 feed
18 watch 19 shines 20 dream
### Exercise 4
1 She doesn't eat meat.
2 My husband doesn't like cold
  weather.
3 He doesn't speak Arabic.
4 He doesn't like his boss.
5 She doesn't have a stamp.
6 She doesn't have any money.
7 The lift doesn't work.
8 It doesn't use petrol.
9 He doesn't listen to me.
10 The bus doesn't stop here.
### Exercise 5
1 I don't have a watch.
2 I don't have a car.
3 You don't like cheese.
4 I don't want to go out tonight.
5 I don't know the answer.
6 We don't have a garden.
7 I don't love you.
8 I don't have any money.
9 I don't like the rain.
10 I don't like the sun.

## UNIT 7
### Exercise 1
1 Do you like eggs?
2 Do you watch a lot of TV?
3 Does he come to work by bus?
4 Do you take sugar in your tea?
5 Does she want a dog?
6 Do you have any brothers or
  sisters?
7 Do you have any money?
8 Does this train go to Tokyo?
9 Do you live near the sea?
10 Do you know her telephone
   number?
11 Do you own a car?
12 Does he know the answers?
### Exercise 2
1 Do you like my dress? No, I
  don't.
2 Do you like Indian food? Yes, I
  do.
3 Do you eat a lot of fruit? No, I
  don't.
4 Does Sally play tennis? No, she
  doesn't.
5 Do you want to hear a joke? No, I
  don't.

6 Do you have a computer at home?
  Yes, I do.
7 Do you make your own bread?
  No, I don't.
8 Does your sister like her job? Yes,
  she does.
9 Do we have any stamps? No, we
  don't.
10 Do you love me? Yes, I do.
11 Do you want a cup of tea? No, I
   don't.
12 Do they like chocolate? Yes, they
   do.
### Exercise 3
1h Where do you work?
2c When do you start work?
3b Where do you live?
4e What do you have for breakfast?
5d What does your dog have for
   breakfast?
6g What does your brother do?
7f What do you want to do tonight?
8a Why do you walk to work?
### Exercise 4
1 a) The earth moves round the
     sun.
  b) Does the sun move round the
     earth?
2 a) I love you. b) Do I love you?
3 a) This train stops at Venice.
  b) Does this train stop at Venice?
4 a) You play golf on holiday.
  b) Do you play golf on holiday?
5 a) She always does all the
     exercises.
  b) Does she always do all the
     exercises?
6 a) They like the colour of that
     house.
  b) Do they like the colour of that
     house?
7 a) She always arrives late.
  b) Does she always arrive late?
8 a) You feel ill today.
  b) Do you feel ill today?
9 a) They read interesting books
     on that course.
  b) Do they read interesting books
     on that course?
10 a) Those chairs cost £300.
   b) Do those chairs cost £300?
11 a) That shop sells bread.
   b) Does that shop sell bread?
12 a) That film tells the true story of
      the war.
   b) Does that film tell the true
      story of the war?
13 a) Your car goes fast.
   b) Does your car go fast?
14 a) He enjoys the work at that
      company.
   b) Does he enjoy the work at that
      company?
15 a) She's got very nice friends.
   b) Has she got very nice friends?
16 a) It makes you angry.
   b) Does it make you angry?
17 a) You live in Rome.
   b) Do you live in Rome?

18 a) She listens to 'pop' music.
   b) Does she listen to 'pop'
      music?
19 a) They want to go to the moon.
   b) Do they want to go to the
      moon?
20 a) The sun rises in the East.
   b) Does the sun rise in the East?
### Exercise 5
2 don't 3 does 4 don't 5 don't 6 Does
7 don't 8 Do 9 don't 10 doesn't
11 doesn't 12 Do 13 don't 14 don't
15 don't 16 don't 17 don't 18 doesn't

## UNIT 8
### Exercise 1
2 talking 3 going 4 coming 5 taking
6 making 7 moving 8 shopping
9 stopping 10 planning 11 sitting
12 getting 13 breaking 14 laughing
15 staying
### Exercise 2:
2 singing 3 reading 4 writing, telling
5 playing 6 answering 7 cooking
8 talking 9 learning 10 trying
### Exercise 3
1 Mrs Johnson is sitting in her
  garden.
2 Mr Johnson is playing the piano.
3 The sun is shining.
4 Three dogs are swimming in the
  river.
5 A cat is sleeping in a tree.
6 Some men are talking near the
  post office.
7 Dr Jones is working in her office.
8 A policeman is walking down the
  street.
9 Fiona is taking a photograph of
  her brother.
10 Some boys are eating ice-cream
   near the school.
11 Some birds are flying over the
   park.
12 A little girl is riding her bicycle.
13 Jane and Peter are drinking
   coffee in the bar.
14 Maria is shopping for her dinner.
15 My son is talking to his friends
   on the phone.
### Exercise 4
1 **Fred:** Are you reading a
             magazine?
  **You:** No, I'm not reading a
             magazine. I'm reading a
             book about English
             grammar, Fred.
2 **Fred:** Are you eating chocolate?
  **You:** No, I am not eating
             chocolate. I am trying to
             understand the present
             continuous, Fred.
3 **Fred:** Are you listening to the
             radio?
  **You:** No, I'm not listening to
             the radio. I'm doing my
             homework, Fred.
4 **Fred:** Are you playing the
             piano?
  **You:** No, I'm not playing the
             piano. I'm writing the

answers to this exercise,
Fred.
5 **Fred:** Are you listening to me?
  **You:** No, I'm not listening to
             you. I'm putting down the
             phone, Fred. Goodbye!
### Exercise 5
1 What are you eating?
  I'm eating a sandwich.
2 What is she watching?
  She's watching a film.
3 What are you writing?
  I'm writing a letter to my cousin.
4 What are you drinking?
  I'm drinking some lemonade.
5 What are they reading?
  They're reading Grammar
  Workbook 1.
6 What is she doing?
  She's making bread in the
  kitchen.
7 What are you looking for?
  I'm looking for my yellow socks.
8 Why are you laughing?
  The cat is eating your dinner!
9 Where is he going?
  He's going to the library.
10 What are they listening to?
   They're listening to the radio.

## UNIT 9
### Exercise 1
1 At 8.00, she's having breakfast.
2 At 9.00, she's going to the bank
  for some money.
3 At 10.30, she's making some
  bread.
4 At 11.30, she's buying some fruit
  at the greengrocer's.
5 At 1.00, she's meeting Joanna for
  lunch.
6 At 3.00, she's washing some
  shirts.
7 At 3.30, she's taking the car to the
  garage.
8 At 5.00, she's cleaning the
  windows in the kitchen.
9 At 6.45, she's playing squash
  with Jenny.
10 At 8.15, she's cooking dinner for
   the family.
11 At 9.30, she's washing up.
12 At 11.00 she's having a shower.
13 At 11.30, she's going to bed.
14 At 11.31, she's going to sleep!
### Exercise 2
1 In March, I'm fishing in Scotland.
2 In April, I'm learning German in
  Berlin.
3 In May, I'm taking my boat down
  the Nile.
4 In June, I'm getting engaged.
5 In July, I'm making a film in
  Hollywood.
6 In August, I'm walking from
  South Africa to Morocco.
7 In September, I'm getting
  married.
8 In October, we're climbing
  Mount Kilimanjaro together.

9  In November, we're buying a house.
10  In December, I'm selling my boat!

**Exercise 3**
1  When is she going to Hong Kong?
   She is going to Hong Kong on Tuesday.
2  When is the train leaving?
   The train is leaving at half past three.
3  When are you playing golf with Fred?
   We are playing tomorrow afternoon.
4  What are you doing tomorrow?
   I am cleaning the house.
5  When are you meeting your girlfriend?
   I am meeting her at one o'clock.
6  Where are you meeting your uncle?
   I am meeting him at a café.
7  What are you doing tonight?
   I am washing my hair.
8  Where are we having dinner tonight?
   We are having dinner at that new Spanish restaurant near the river.
9  Why aren't you coming to the party?
   I'm studying for my exams.
10  Why aren't you studying tonight?
   I am going to a party!

**Exercise 4**
1  How are we getting to the airport?
   We're getting there by train.
2  How are we getting to China?
   We're getting there by plane.
3  How are they going to the island?
   They're getting there by ferry.
4  How are they getting to the top of the mountain?
   They're getting there by the ski lift.
5  How is the President coming to the meeting?
   She's coming here by helicopter.
6  How are you going to the supermarket?
   I'm going there by bus.
7  How are you getting home?
   I'm getting there by car.
8  How am I getting home?
   You're getting there on foot.

**Exercise 5**
1 are you doing 2 I'm going 3 isn't coming 4 is he doing 5 he's painting 6 is teaching 7 Are you visiting 8 I'm staying 9 they're starting 10 Is Stan changing 11 he's stopping 12 is he doing 13 he's studying 14 he's going 15 you're moving 16 are you going 17 is working 18 is designing 19 Is he building 20 is doing

## UNIT 10
**Exercise 1**
1  It's snowing.
2  It snows every day in the winter.
3  He eats an apple every day.
4  She usually starts work at 8.30. But she is starting at 9.00 today.
5  The sun is shining.
6  In Japanese, 'mushi mushi' means 'hello'.
7  My teacher speaks four languages.
8  He usually goes to bed at 10.00.
9  I need some help!
10  He usually wakes up at 7.00. And he normally goes to work by bus. But he woke up at 8.33 this morning. So, today he's taking a taxi!

**Exercise 2**
1 hates, eats, loves, cooks 2 washes 3 is washing 4 Do you like 5 is crying 6 does this word mean 7 Do you know 8 studies 9 go 10 I'm having

## REVISION TEST 1
**Units 1-5**
1 B 2 C 3 C 4 C 5 A 6 C 7 A 8 C 9 A 10 B 11 B 12 B 13 A 14 A 15 B 16 C
**Units 6-7**
17 C 18 C 19 A 20 C 21 B 22 B 23 C 24 A
**Units 8-9**
25 C 26 B 27 C 28 B 29 B 30 B 31 C 32 A 33 C
**Unit 10**
34 A 35 A 36 C 37 A 38 C 39 B 40 C

## UNIT 11
**Exercise 1**
1 Open 2 Say 3 Fasten 4 Look 5 Hurry 6 Help 7 Stay 8 Have 9 Turn 10 Sleep 11 Bring 12 Be 13 Buy 14 Take 15 Give

**Exercise 2**
1  Don't eat biscuits in bed!
2  Don't listen to the radio after 10 o'clock!
3  Don't eat food on the stairs!
4  Don't talk at breakfast!
5  Don't use hot water in the bath!
6  Don't ask me any questions!
7  Don't sleep with the window open!
8  Don't use the telephone!
9  Don't forget your key!
10  Don't come in after 11 o'clock!
11  Don't leave anything in your room!
12  Don't bring children to the hotel!
13  Don't ask for more food at dinner!
14  Don't stay in your room after 9.30 in the morning!
15  Don't forget to enjoy your holiday!

**Exercise 3**
1 Go, Buy 2 Wash, dry 3 Open, Take, Find 4 Cut 5 Put 6 Eat, say

**Exercise 4**
1 dry 2 buy 3 read 4 wear 5 eat

6 study 7 make 8 open 9 watch 10 buy

**Exercise 5**
1  Sleep well!
2  Take my umbrella!
3  Stop the car now!
4  Open the window!
5  Drink a cup of tea!
6  Go to the dentist!
7  Wear the old ones!
8  Yes, sit down, please!
9  Buy some apples, please.

## UNIT 12
**Exercise 1**
1  The flat was cold.
2  The cafés were full.
3  The bank wasn't open.
4  That question was easy.
5  They were tired.
6  The book was interesting.
7  The trains were slow.
8  The weather was good.
9  The radio was on.
10  The bags were very heavy.
11  The water was very cold.
12  The water wasn't very hot.
13  He was very strong.
14  I was very tired.
15  My boss was very friendly.

**Exercise 2**
1  Was the restaurant busy?
2  Were the waiters friendly?
3  Were the knives and forks clean?
4  Was the soup hot?
5  Were the vegetables fresh?
6  Was the ice-cream OK?
7  Was the coffee good?
8  Was the meal expensive?

**Exercise 3**
1  When was the party? It was last night.
2  Where was the party? It was at Tina's house.
3  Where were you last night? I was at home.
4  When were you in New Zealand? We were there in 1993.
5  Who was Michelangelo? He was a famous painter.
6  Who was your first teacher? Mrs Heiber was my first teacher.

**Exercise 4**
1 Was 2 was Chinese 3 Was 4 easy 5 Was 6 funny 7 Was 8 was small 9 Was 10 was full 11 Were 12 were cheap

**Exercise 5**
1 Were, wasn't, was 2 were, weren't, were 3 was, was, were 4 weren't 5 were, weren't was, was, were

## UNIT 13
**Exercise 1**
1 worked 2 played 3 talked 4 wrote 5 ate 6 finished 7 read 8 found 9 drank 10 wanted 11 spoke 12 answered 13 ran 14 drove 15 flew 16 cried 17 tried 18 came 19 left 20 talked

**Exercise 2**
2 cooked 3 painted 4 swam 5 washed 6 worked 7 went 8 got 9 ran 10 read

11 built 12 wrote 13 sang 14 cycled 15 watched 16 slept

**Exercise 3**
2 (i) painted 3 (a) took 4 (e) built 5 (h) jumped 6 (g) wrote 7 (b) invented 8 (f) sent 9 (d) opened

**Exercise 4**
1 lost, climbed 2 wrote 3 made 4 played, drank, talked, went, took, went 5 waited 6 bought, took 7 met 8 sent, received 9 read, watched 10 started, finished, fell, woke

**Exercise 5**
1 lived 2 joined 3 promoted 4 led 5 explored 6 made 7 returned 8 married 9 had 10 studied 11 grew 12 wanted 13 paid 14 found 15 went 16 planned 17 had 18 arrived 19 saw 20 got 21 had 22 became 23 died 24 found

## UNIT 14
**Exercise 1**
1  I didn't eat your apple.
2  I didn't buy a new car.
3  She didn't understand the question.
4  They didn't go to Germany.
5  We didn't watch television.
6  I didn't like the film.
7  He didn't read the newspaper.
8  The bus didn't stop.
9  She didn't telephone me.
10  They didn't know the words of the song.
11  They didn't drink coffee.
12  She didn't find the money.
13  I didn't lose my keys.
14  The dog didn't run away.
15  We didn't play tennis.

**Exercise 2**
1 didn't eat 2 didn't rain 3 didn't read 4 didn't drink 5 didn't comb 6 didn't finish 7 didn't wear 8 didn't play 9 didn't catch 10 didn't spend 11 didn't win 12 didn't return 13 didn't take 14 didn't sleep 15 didn't put

**Exercise 3**
1  Did you go to the beach?
2  Did you swim in the sea?
3  Did you stay in a nice hotel?
4  Did you eat a lot of ice-cream?
5  Did you meet any interesting people?
6  Did you go to Florence?
7  Did you buy some Italian shoes?
8  Did you send any postcards?
9  Did you drink a lot of coffee?
10  Did you buy me a present?
11  Did you sit in the sun?
12  Did you go dancing?
13  Did you read any books?
14  Did you like your holiday?
15  Did you want to come home?

**Exercise 4**
1  Where did you go on holiday last year?
2  When did the train arrive at the station?

3 How did you get here?

4 Why did you buy 15 blue pencils?

5 Who did they invite to the party?

6 When did Marconi send the first radio message?

7 When did Daguerre take the first photograph?

8 Where did Columbus go in 1492?

9 What did Mr Rolls and Mr Royce build in 1906?

10 What time did the lesson begin yesterday?

11 When did she leave?

12 Where did you find that interesting painting?

13 When did your wife become a teacher?

14 What did you have for dinner?

15 When did you buy your house?

## Exercise 5

1 Did she do the homework?
Yes, she did.

2 Did you eat all the biscuits?
No, I didn't.

3 Did they meet you at the station?
No, they didn't.

4 Did he buy a new car?
Yes, he did.

5 Did they win the match?
No, they didn't.

6 Did he make his bed this morning?
No, he didn't.

7 Did Jenny make this bread?
Yes, she did.

8 Did it snow last month?
Yes, it did.

9 Did they wash up last night?
Yes, they did.

10 Did they enjoy the holiday?
No, they didn't.

11 Did she buy a new coat?
No, she didn't

12 Did you find your dog?
Yes, I did.

13 Did they go to France?
No, they didn't.

14 Did he like the film?
No, he didn't.

15 Did she catch her train?
Yes, she did.

## UNIT 15

### Exercise 1

1 was making 2 was washing 3 were putting 4 was sleeping 5 was cooking 6 was putting 7 were buying 8 was looking 9 was crying 10 was watching, was eating

### Exercise 2

1 was raining 2 was going 3 was waiting 4 was watching 5 was looking 6 was watching 7 was buying 8 was snowing 9 was driving 10 was wearing

### Exercise 3

1 were running, fell 2 was eating, came 3 were playing, started 4 were driving, asked 5 was making, rang 6 was snowing, arrived 7 was living,

saw 8 were walking, met 9 was listening, had 10 was raining, went

### Exercise 4

2 was standing 3 were you doing 4 was waiting 5 were you going 6 was going 7 was the first robber wearing 8 was wearing 9 was the first robber carrying 10 was carrying 11 were you sitting 12 was sitting 13 were you doing 14 was drinking 15 was the second robber wearing 16 was wearing 17 was the second robber carrying 18 was carrying 19 were you working 20 was working 21 was making

## UNIT 16

### Exercise 1

1 She's spent all her money.

2 They've bought a big house near the sea.

3 I've started to learn English.

4 He's drunk ten cups of tea today.

5 They've eaten all my chocolate!

6 I've made a few mistakes.

7 I've done a lot of work today.

8 I've put a hot-water bottle in the bed.

9 They've made some toast.

10 She's taken the dog for a walk.

11 He's missed the bus!

12 She's lost her passport!

### Exercise 2

1 She hasn't answered my letter.

2 They haven't read all of the book.

3 He hasn't sent me the money.

4 We haven't understood this very well.

5 It hasn't rained for two weeks.

6 We haven't sung this song for years.

7 They haven't planned their holiday.

8 She hasn't read the newspaper.

9 I haven't been to Pakistan.

10 I haven't climbed Mount Everest.

11 We haven't painted the bathroom.

12 The dog hasn't eaten its food.

### Exercise 3

2 eaten 3 drunk 4 sold 5 bought 6 asked

### Exercise 4

2 gone 3 been 4 gone 5 gone 6 been 7 gone 8 been 9 gone 10 gone

### Exercise 5

2f ... she's just drunk a cup of coffee.

3a ... I've just fallen in the river.

4e ... I've just run 23 kilometres.

5c ... she's just been out in the snow.

6d ... they've just finished this exercise.

7b ... I've just eaten three pizzas.

## UNIT 17

### Exercise 1

1 Has Jackie eaten all the biscuits?

2 Have you read this book?

3 Have you seen my green pencil?

4 Have you made your bed?

5 Has she opened the letter?

6 Has Jim gone to the bank?

7 Have you thanked her for the present?

8 Have you cleaned your shoes?

9 Has she bought a new piano?

10 Has he washed the car?

### Exercise 2

1 Have you ever worked in a restaurant?

2 Have you ever taken a photograph of an elephant?

3 Have you ever slept on a train?

4 Have you ever washed your shirt in a river?

5 Have you ever told a lie?

6 Have you ever been in a desert?

### Exercise 3

1 Have you ever driven a Ferrari?
Yes, I have.

2 Have you ever been to Australia?
Yes, I have.

3 Have you ever written a book?
No, I haven't.

4 Have you ever written a letter to a film star?
No, I haven't.

5 Have you ever given a long interview.
No, I haven't.

### Exercise 4

1 Have you ever played cricket.
No, I've never played cricket. But I've played baseball.

2 Has she ever eaten Indonesian food?
No, she's never eaten Indonesian food. But she's eaten Thai food.

3 Have they ever met your brother?
No, they've never met my brother. But they've met my sister.

4 Has he ever been on an aeroplane?
No, he's never been on an aeroplane. But he's been in a helicopter.

5 Have you ever swum in the sea?
No, I've never swum in the sea. But, I've swum in a river.

6 Have you ever driven a train?
No, I've never driven a train. But I've driven a car.

### Exercise 5

1 Have you found your yellow socks yet?
No, I haven't found my yellow socks yet.

2 Have they cleaned the windows yet?
No, they haven't cleaned the windows yet.

3 Has the train arrived yet?
No, the train hasn't arrived yet.

4 Have you had lunch yet?
No, I haven't had lunch yet.

5 Have you made any mistakes yet?
No, I haven't made any mistakes yet.

6 Has she read the magazine yet?
No, she hasn't read the magazine yet.

7 Have you finished this exercise yet?
No, I haven't finished this exercise yet.

8 Have you taken the dog for a walk yet?
No, I haven't taken the dog for a walk yet.

### Exercise 6

1 g Have you ever seen the Amazon?

2 e Has Francesca gone to Milan by plane?

3 a Have you seen my newspaper?

4 b Have you given the dog its food?

5 f Have you washed your hair?

6 c Have you bought some new shoes?

7 d Have you had dinner yet?

## UNIT 18

### Exercise 1

1 I'm going to 2 She's going to 3 They're going to 4 I'm going to 5 I'm going to 6 He's going to 7 We're going to 8 She's going to 9 She's going to 10 He's going to 11 We're going to 12 He's going to 13 I'm going to 14 We're going to 15 She's going to

### Exercise 2

1 On Monday, we're going to play tennis and swim.

2 On Tuesday, we're going to eat fish and chips and see a film.

3 On Wednesday, we're going to walk to the mountains and have a picnic.

4 On Thursday, we're going to walk in the countryside and ride a horse.

5 On Friday, we're going to take a boat and visit some islands.

6 On Saturday, we're going to take a taxi to the airport and fly home.

### Exercise 3

1 aren't going to 2 aren't going to 3 isn't going to 4 aren't going to 5 isn't going to 6 isn't going to 7 I'm not going to 8 isn't going to 9 isn't going to 10 aren't going to

### Exercise 4

1 Are they going to buy a dog?

2 Are you going to eat all that pizza?

3 Is he going to play golf at the weekend?

4 Are you going to have a holiday this year?

5 Is it going to snow tomorrow?

6 Are you going to tell me the truth?

7 Is he going to win the game?

8 Are you going to wash the dishes?

9 Are you going to build a snowman this winter?

10 Are they going to sing that song again?

## Exercise 5

3 Am I going to marry my boyfriend Tim?
4 Yes. And you're going to have nine children.
5 Are we going to live in the city?
6 No. You're going to live in the countryside.
7 Are we going to live in a flat?
8 No. You're going to live in a big house.
9 Are we going to have a garden?
10 Yes. You're going to have a beautiful garden with lots of trees.
11 Are we going to have lots of pets?
12 Yes. You're going to have 3 dogs, 6 cats and a parrot!
13 Are we going to have lots of holidays?
14 Yes. You're going to travel all over the world.
15 Are we going to be happy?
16 Yes. You're going to be very happy.
17 Are we going to be rich?
18 Perhaps. But first you're going to pay me £100! Thank you.

## UNIT 19
### Exercise 1

1 I'll 2 I'll 3 I'll 4 I'll 5 I won't 6 I won't 7 I won't 8 I'll 9 I'll 10 I'll 11 I'll 12 I'll

### Exercise 2

2 will eat 3 will be 4 will work 5 will fly 6 will speak 7 will drink 8 will wear 9 will spend 10 will drive 11 will use 12 will die

### Exercise 3

2 When will the holiday end?
   The holiday will end on June 11th.
3 What will the temperature be at that time of year?
   The temperature will be about 25°C.
4 Where will we stay?
   You will stay in a five star hotel.
5 How will we get there?
   You will fly there from Manchester Airport.
6 How long will the flight be?
   The flight will be four hours.
7 How will we get from the airport to the hotel?
   You will get to the hotel by taxi.
8 Where will we have breakfast?
   You will have breakfast in the hotel dining room.
9 Where will we have lunch?
   You will have lunch on the beach.
10 Where will we have dinner?
   You will have dinner in one of the local restaurants.
11 What will we do there?
   You will sit in the sun, swim and eat.
12 How much will the holiday cost?
   It will cost £500 per person.

## Exercise 4

1 Shall 2 Shall 3 Shall 4 Shall 5 Will 6 Shall 7 Will 8 Will 9 Will 10 Will 11 Shall 12 Shall

### Exercise 5

1 Shall we 2 Shall we 3 Shall I 4 Shall I 5 Shall we, shall we 6 Shall I, shall we

## UNIT 20
### Exercise 1

1 must 2 mustn't 3 mustn't 4 must 5 must 6 must, mustn't 7 must 8 must 9 must 10 mustn't, must 11 mustn't 12 must

### Exercise 2

1 has to 2 have to 3 have to 4 had to 5 had to 6 has to 7 had to 8 have to 9 had to 10 had to 11 has to 12 have to

### Exercise 3

1 Do we have to answer every question in the exam?
2 Does he have to work on Saturdays?
3 Does she have to wear glasses to read?
4 Do you have to pay to go to the doctor's? Or is it free?
5 Do we have to pay to use the library? Or is it free?
6 Do you have to wear a uniform at your school? Or can you wear jeans?
7 Did you have to do homework last night?
8 Did you have to use a dictionary? Or did you know all the words?
9 Did they have to buy a map? Or did they know the way?
10 Did you have to use a key. Or was the door open?

### Exercise 4

1 Must you drive on the left or the right in Australia?
2 I'm going to Canada. Must I get a visa?
3 Must we go by boat? Or can we fly to the island?
4 I'm tired. Must we go to the party?
5 I hate vegetables! Must I eat all these carrots?

### Exercise 5

1 She doesn't have to work.
2 He doesn't have to buy apples.
3 You don't have to shout.
4 You don't have to wear a tie here.
5 I didn't have to go to the office yesterday.
6 I didn't have to buy a ticket for the concert yesterday.
7 They didn't have to take an umbrella yesterday.
8 This is a hotel and we're on holiday! You don't have to make the beds today. You don't have to wash the dishes today. You don't have to clean the floors today. You don't have to tidy the room

today. You don't have to cook three meals today.

### Exercise 6

1 mustn't 2 don't have to 3 mustn't 4 mustn't 5 don't have to

## UNIT 21
### Exercise 1

1 She can play basketball but she can't play golf.
2 He can ride a bike but he can't drive a car.
3 My brother can remember faces but he can't remember names.
4 Her uncle can play the violin but he can't play the piano.
5 My sister can swim but she can't dance.
6 Her husband can dance but he can't swim.
7 I can make toast but I can't cook spaghetti.
8 My aunt can speak Turkish but she can't speak Russian.
9 Julia can sing but she can't paint.
10 Andrew can use a typewriter but he can't use a computer.
11 I can walk but I can't run.
12 My wife can swim but she can't drive.
13 Her dog can catch a ball but it can't catch a stick.
14 He can work in the day but he can't work at night.
15 Her sister can sing in private but she can't sing in public.

### Exercise 2

1 Can he play tennis?
2 Can you swim?
3 Can you make bread?
4 Can your uncle ride a bicycle?
5 Can you use a computer?
6 Can you work at night?
7 Can you understand this question?
8 Can you ride a horse?
9 Can people in your country cook well?
10 Can you drink tea without sugar?
11 Can she speak Spanish?
12 Can you read music?
13 Can your brother make spaghetti too?
14 Can he sleep in the day?
15 Can they both play the violin?

### Exercise 3

2 f 3 b 4 e 5 d 6 a 7 h 8 g 9 c

### Exercise 4

1 Can you waterski? Yes, I can.
2 Can you drive a bus? No, I can't.
3 Can your sister read Arabic. Yes, she can.
4 Can you remember his telephone number? No, I can't.
5 Can you remember his address? No, I can't.
6 Can you sleep with the light on? Yes, I can.
7 Can you sleep with the window open? Yes, I can.

8 Can your parents play golf? No, they can't.
9 Can your cat jump from tree to tree? Yes, it can.
10 Can you climb a tree? No, I can't.
11 Can you find your keys? No, I can't.
12 Can she play the piano? No, she can't.
13 Can you work twelve hours a day? Yes, I can.
14 Can your father see without glasses? No, he can't.
15 Can your dog run very fast? Yes, it can.

### Exercise 5

2 can't 3 can't 4 can 5 can 6 Can 7 can't 8 can't 9 can 10 can 11 can 12 Can 13 can't

## UNIT 22
### Exercise 1

1 Where 2 What 3 What 4 Where 5 When 6 When 7 What 8 What

### Exercise 2

1 How many 2 How many 3 How much 4 How many 5 How much 6 How much 7 How many 8 How many

### Exercise 3

1 What did you wear?
2 When did you arrive?
3 What did you eat?
4 How many did you eat?
5 When did James arrive?
6 Where did you sit?
7 What did you give Sally for her birthday?
8 How many did she take?

### Exercise 4

1 Which dress do you prefer, the yellow one or the blue one?
2 Which apple do you want, the big one or the small one?
3 Which drink do you prefer, tea or coffee?
4 Which bus do you take to work, the number 24 or the number 40?
5 Which city do you prefer, Hong Kong or Beijing?

### Exercise 5

1 Which flour did you buy, the white or the brown?
2 Which restaurant shall we go to, The Rice Garden or Pizza Now?
3 Which pencil can I use, this one or that one?
4 Which room did they paint, the bedroom or the kitchen?
5 Which road shall we take, the left or the right?

### Exercise 6

1 How long 2 How tall 3 How often 4 How old 5 How fast 6 How far 7 How often 8 How far

## UNIT 23
### Exercise 1

1 Who are you talking to?
2 Who are you going to the cinema with?

3 Who telephoned Fred?
4 Who did Fred telephone?
5 Who wrote to Francesca?
6 Who did Francesca write to?
7 Who played tennis?
8 Who did you play tennis with?
9 Who did you invite to the party?
10 Who invited you to the party?

**Exercise 2**

3 Who kisses Julietta?
4 Who has also watched the game?
5 Who did Carlos telephone?
6 Who does Juan tell?
7 Who did Lita tell?
8 Who was cooking the dinner?
9 Who was very excited?
10 Who did Paulo tell?
11 Who were having a quarrel?
12 Who forgot to tell Paulo about the game?

**REVISION TEST 2**

**Units 11–14**

1 A 2 B 3 A 4 B 5 A 6 C 7 B 8 C 9 A 10 C 11 A

**Units 15–17**

12 B 13 B 14 A 15 C 16 C 17 C 18 B 19 C 20 A 21 B 22 C

**Units 18–19**

23 A 24 B 25 A 26 B 27 A 28 C

**Units 20–23**

29 C 30 C 31 B 32 A 33 A 34 C 35 A 36 C

**UNIT 24**

**Exercise 1**

2 an 3 a 4 a 5 an 6 an 7 a 8 a 9 an 10 a 11 a 12 a 13 an 14 a 15 an, a 16 a 17 a 18 a 19 an 20 a

**Exercise 2**

2 a 3 a 4 a 5 an 6 an 7 an 8 a, a, an 9 an 10 an 11 an 12 a 13 a 14 a 15 an 16 a, a 17 a 18 a, an 19 a, a 20 an, a

**Exercise 3**

1 He has a birthday party once a year.
2 There is a train to Tokyo three times an hour.
3 He watches television five hours a day.
4 She telephones her brother three or four times a month.
5 They go to Spain twice a year.
6 We study English four times a week.
7 He was driving at 225 kilometres an hour!
8 My uncle works twelve hours a day.
9 The balloon flies at 30 kilometres an hour.
10 We paid $3 a kilo for the tomatoes.
11 We eat fish once a week.
12 That programme is on television twice a day.
13 His mother phones once a day.
14 They go on holiday three times a year.
15 We spend a third of our lives sleeping.

**Exercise 4**

2 a 3 a 4 a 5 an 6 an 7 a 8 a 9 a 10 a 11 a 12 an

**Exercise 5**

2 a 3 an 4 a 5 an 6 a 7 a

**Exercise 6**

1 a dog 2 an arm 3 a shoe 4 an invitation 5 an orange/an apple 6 a bank 7 an ear 8 a name 9 a holiday 10 an apple/an orange 11 a bottle 12 a train 13 an envelope 14 an evening 15 a beautiful garden 16 a car 17 an umbrella 18 a shirt 19 a strange animal 20 an office

**UNIT 25**

**Exercise 1**

1 a, a, The, the 2 a, a, the, the 3 a, a, the, the, a , an, the, the

**Exercise 2**

1 meat 2 the meat 3 milk 4 the milk 5 water, chocolate 6 the water 7 love, money 8 The homework 9 cities 10 The photographs 11 photographs 12 The coffee 13 the coffee 14 dogs 15 friends 16 cars 17 coffee, the juice 18 the blue car, the red car 19 water 20 the people

**Exercise 3**

1 The, Ø 2 Ø 3 Ø, Ø 4 Ø 5 The, the 6 Ø 7 Ø 8 the 9 Ø, Ø, Ø 10 Ø 11 the 12 The, the 13 the, the 14 The 15 the, Ø, Ø

**Exercise 4**

2 the, Ø 3 Ø 4 the 5 Ø 6 the 7 the 8 the 9 The 10 Ø 11 the 12 Ø 13 The, the 14 Ø 15 the

**Exercise 5**

2 Ø 3 the 4 Ø 5 the 6 a 7 the 8 the 9 the 10 a 11 the 12 a 13 the 14 the 15 a 16 the

**UNIT 26**

**Exercise 1**

2 that 3 this 4 that 5 these 6 that 7 those 8 this 9 these 10 that 11 those 12 this 13 those 14 this 15 these 16 that 17 that 18 those

**Exercise 2**

1 this 2 This, these 3 these 4 this 5 this 6 this 7 these 8 this 9 This 10 These 11 these 12 this 13 this 14 This 15 these 16 this 17 These 18 these 19 These 20 this

**Exercise 3**

1 those 2 that 3 those 4 that 5 those 6 that 7 that 8 Those 9 that 10 those 11 those 12 that 13 that 14 those 15 That, those 16 that 17 that 18 those 19 those 20 that, those

**Exercise 4**

2 This is a window.
3 This is a sandwich.
4 This is a cup of tea.
5 This is a magazine.
6 These are tickets.
7 Those are cows.
8 That is a field.
9 That is a river.
10 That is a bridge.
11 That is a tree.

12 Those are mountains.
13 Those are clouds.

**UNIT 27**

**Exercise 1**

1 It 2 She 3 We 4 It 5 He 6 It 7 They 8 It 9 They 10 She 11 It 12 It 13 They 14 It

**Exercise 2**

1 them 2 it 3 her 4 them 5 it 6 it 7 us 8 him 9 it 10 them 11 it 12 them 13 it 14 it

**Exercise 3**

3 He 4 They 5 He 6 She 7 She 8 They 9 He 10 They 11 He 12 We

**Exercise 4**

1 We often eat Italian food.
2 They often eat sushi.
3 I can't drink it!
4 She loved it.
5 We write to him every year.
6 He brings us a present every year.
7 We are meeting him at the station.
8 She played them to us yesterday.

**Exercise 5**

5 I 6 her 7 she 8 me 9 I 10 them 11 they 12 me 13 she 14 them 15 they 16 her 17 She 18 us 19 we 20 her 21 I / She 22 her / me 23 She / I 24 me / her

**UNIT 28**

**Exercise 1**

1 her 2 their 3 my 4 his 5 my 6 her 7 his 8 her 9 their 10 its 11 your 12 our 13 our 14 her 15 her 16 my 17 his 18 their 19 its 20 her

**Exercise 2**

1 my 2 my / my 3 his 4 her 5 your 6 your 7 their 8 his 9 your 10 their 11 her 12 my 13 our 14 their 15 His 16 her 17 our 18 our, its 19 her, her 20 my

**Exercise 3**

1 mine 2 yours 3 hers 4 yours 5 theirs 6 ours 7 yours 8 theirs 9 mine 10 his 11 yours 12 hers 13 his 14 mine 15 theirs

**Exercise 4**

1 yours 2 ours 3 mine 4 hers 5 his 6 theirs 7 hers 8 yours 9 yours 10 mine 11 his 12 theirs 13 mine 14 ours 15 yours

**Exercise 5**

1 yours 2 yours, mine 3 Her, ours 4 My, theirs 5 ours, theirs 6 My, yours 7 Their, ours 8 Our, theirs 9 Our, yours 10 Our, yours 11 Your, mine 12 her

**UNIT 29**

**Exercise 1**

1 Jack's house 2 Gina's car, Carol's motorbike 3 the men's coats, Jenny's bedroom, the women's coats, Frank's bedroom 4 Fred's coat, Frank's room 5 Carol's coat, Frank's room, Fred's coat 6 Jenny's bedroom, Carol's coat 7 Carol's coat 8 Fred's boss, Carol's lipstick, Fred's face

**Exercise 2**

1 at the greengrocer's 2 at the grocer's

3 at the newsagent's 4 at John's house 5 at David's school 6 at the chemist's 7 at Daisy's house 8 at Richard's house 9 at Peter's guest house 10 at Fred's club 11 In Jane's garden 12 At the jeweller's

**Exercise 3**

1 I don't like the colour of that shirt.
2 What is the capital of Thailand?
3 I fell asleep in the middle of the film.
4 What is the meaning of that word?
5 I'll meet you at the front of the station.
6 What is the name of that mountain?
7 What is the telephone number of the restaurant?
8 What is the address of the White House?
9 I met Jenny in the spring of 1997.
10 This is a photograph of my school.
11 I like the taste of this food.
12 The garden is at the back of the house.

**Exercise 4**

1 Whose book is this? It is Tina's.
2 Whose books are these? They're Tina's.
3 Whose dog is that? It's my sister's.
4 Whose biscuits are these? They're Robert's?
5 Whose parrot is that? It's my uncle's.
6 Whose radio is this? It's Joan's.
7 Whose newspapers are these? They're Aunt Beryl's.
8 Whose computer is that? It's my brother's.
9 Whose CDs are these? They're Harriet's.
10 Whose answers are these? They're mine!
11 Whose keys are those? They're John's.
12 Whose television is this? It's my father's.

**Exercise 5**

1 Whose is that? It's theirs.
2 Whose are these? They're mine.
3 Whose is this? It's mine.
4 Whose is that? It's hers.
5 Whose are these? They're ours.
6 Whose are those? They're hers.
7 Whose is that? It's ours.
8 Whose are these? They're yours.
9 Whose are those? They're his.
10 Whose is this? It's yours.
11 Whose are these? They're his.
12 Whose is that? It's mine.

**UNIT 30**

**Exercise 1**

The uncountable nouns are 1, 8, 9, 14, 16, 20, 21, 23, 25, 26

**Exercise 2**
2 glasses/litres 3 cups/glasses 4 cups
5 pieces/slices 6 spoonfuls
7 pieces 8 bars/pieces 9 items/pieces
10 pieces 11 items/pieces
**Exercise 3**
1 many 2 much 3 many 4 much
5 many 6 much 7 much 8 much
9 many, much 10 many 11 much
12 many 13 many 14 much 15 much
16 many 17 many 18 many 19 much
20 much
**Exercise 4**
1 How many 2 How many 3 How
many 4 How much 5 How much
6 How much 7 How many 8 How
much 9 How many 10 How much
11 How many 12 How many
13 How many 14 How many 15 How
many
**Exercise 5**
1 accidents 2 films 3 homework
4 information 5 furniture 6 tourists
7 scenery 8 money 9 equipment
10 tea 11 coffee 12 music 13 work
14 bread 15 sport 16 time 17 examples 18 water 19 coins 20 meat
**UNIT 31**
**Exercise 1**
1 some 2 some 3 a, some, some,
some, some, a, a, a, some 4 some
5 an, some, a, some, some, a, a
**Exercise 2**
1 Is there any money on the table?
2 Did he buy any books yesterday?
3 Has she already sold any old
furniture?
4 Will they fetch any water?
5 Must he bring any food with him?
6 Have they got any work today?
7 Was there any rain yesterday?
8 Are there any cars parked near the
school?
9 Have they got any visitors?
10 Did he see any on films
television?
**Exercise 3**
1 We don't have any trees in our
garden.
2 We don't have any butter in the
fridge.
3 We don't have any big mountains
near here.
4 They don't have any questions.
5 She doesn't have any news.
6 He doesn't have any flour in the
kitchen cupboard.
7 This town doesn't have any good
cinemas.
8 We didn't have any snow in the
winter.
9 We didn't have any tea on the
plane yesterday.
10 We didn't have any homework to
do yesterday.
**REVISION TEST 3**
**Units 24-25**
1 B 2 A 3 B 4 A 5 B 6 A 7 C 8 C

**Units 26-27**
9 A 10 C 11 A 12 B 13 A 14 C 15 A
16 B
**Units 28-29**
17 C 18 A 19 C 20 A 21 B 22 A
23 C 24 C 25 C 26 C 27 B 28 A
**Units 30-31**
29 A 30 C 31 B 32 C 33 C 34 A 35 C
36 B 37 C 38 B 39 C 40 C
**UNIT 32**
**Exercise 1**
1 This soup smells good.
2 I love those yellow trousers.
3 That white dog looks dangerous.
4 I feel hot.
5 They sound happy.
6 You look tired.
7 Those tourists look very sad.
8 This bread tastes wonderful.
9 They always feel hungry in the
afternoon.
10 I've bought some fresh milk.
**Exercise 2**
2 cold winters 3 expensive restaurant
4 interesting book 5 fresh fruit
6 beautiful beaches 7 friendly people
8 dangerous journey 9 strong tea
10 foreign languages 11 chocolate
biscuits
**Exercise 3**
2 old, brown, plastic
3 beautiful, new, red, Korean
4 nice, new
5 wonderful, old Italian
6 nice, new, yellow
7 small, blue, wooden
8 beautiful, tall, Italian
9 nice, new
10 nice, brown, French, leather
11 beautiful, tall, Italian
12 nice, brown, French, leather
13 lovely, new, Spanish, leather
14 beautiful, tall, Italian
15 lovely, new, Spanish, leather
16 nice, Dutch, wooden
17 blue, American, plastic
18 yellow, cotton
19 beautiful, tall, Italian
20 brown, plastic
21 brown, plastic
**Exercise 4**
1 Kelly is as old as Veronica.
2 Veronica is not as old as Debbie.
3 Debbie is as tall as James.
4 James is as fast as Tim.
5 Tim is not as rich as Tessa.
6 Tessa is not as young as Kelly.
**UNIT 33**
**Exercise 1**
2 darker 3 bigger 4 taller 5 easier
6 harder 7 colder 8 hotter 9 more
important 10 heavier 11 more
interesting 12 happier 13 nicer
14 better 15 more beautiful
**Exercise 2**
1 Fred is taller than Jane.
2 A train is faster than a car.
3 A plane is faster than a train.

4 A bicycle is cheaper than a
motorbike.
5 A motorbike is more expensive
than a bicycle.
6 Africa is hotter than Greenland.
7 A mountain is bigger than a hill.
8 An ocean is bigger than a sea.
9 My boss is richer than me.
10 I am happier than my boss.
11 Tennis is more interesting than
football.
12 Her bedroom is bigger than her
kitchen.
13 A computer is more expensive
than a typewriter.
14 Tea is nicer than coffee.
15 English is more difficult than my
language.
**Exercise 3**
1 cleaner 2 smaller 3 nicer 4 more
comfortable 5 better 6 cheaper 7 more
difficult 8 quicker 9 bigger 10 richer
**Exercise 4**
2 faster 3 hotter 4 cold 5 more
interesting 6 more beautiful 7 worse
8 taller 9 more dangerous 10 easier
**Exercise 5**
1 A cat isn't as strong as an
elephant.
2 Sri Lanka isn't as big as
Indonesia.
3 Jim isn't as tall as Helen.
4 A tomato isn't as sweet as an
apple.
5 A typewriter isn't as expensive as
a computer.
6 I'm not as strong as you.
7 A bicycle isn't as quick as a car.
8 A kilometre isn't as big as a mile.
**UNIT 34**
**Exercise 1**
1 the happiest 2 the most important
3 the most beautiful 4 the biggest
5 the newest 6 the strongest 7 the
hardest 8 the nicest 9 the largest
10 the noisiest 11 the best 12 the
easiest 13 the worst 14 the most
difficult 15 the youngest
**Exercise 2**
1 Guyana is the smallest country in
South America.
2 Greenland is the biggest country
in the world.
3 The Amazon is the longest river
in Brazil.
4 The Sahara is the biggest desert in
Africa.
5 The Atlantic is the biggest ocean
in the world.
6 Kilimanjaro is the highest
mountain in Africa.
7 Kyoto is the most beautiful city in
Japan.
8 New York is the most exciting
city in the world.
9 The Eiffel Tower is the most
famous building in France.
10 Australia is the biggest island in
the world.

**Exercise 3**
1 the most popular 2 the biggest 3 the
most popular 4 the most enjoyable
5 the wettest 6 the driest 7 the shortest
8 the longest 9 the strongest 10 the
hottest
**Exercise 4**
1 the most enjoyable, had 2 the
funniest, heard 3 the best, cooked
4 the biggest, caught 5 the most
beautiful, visited 6 the best, seen 7 the
most interesting, read 8 the most
dangerous, done 9 the worst, taken
10 the most useful, bought
**Exercise 5**
1 the most interesting, the most
exciting, the cleanest, the most
beautiful
2 the best, the quickest, the most
enjoyable, the cheapest
3 the most expensive, the tallest,
the loudest, the dirtiest, the
noisiest, the coldest
**UNIT 35**
**Exercise 1**
1 badly 2 carefully 3 hard
4 beautifully 5 fast 6 well 7 easily
8 heavily 9 slowly 10 happily
11 quietly 12 badly 13 quickly 14 fast
15 well
**Exercise 2**
1 carefully 2 quietly 3 fast 4 badly
5 well 6 nervously 7 beautifully
8 badly 9 clearly 10 noisily, nicely,
angrily 11 quickly 12 carefully
13 hard 14 angrily 15 well
**Exercise 3**
1 well 2 good 3 well 4 well 5 good,
well 6 well 7 good 8 good, well 9 well
10 well 11 well 12 good 13 well
14 well 15 good
**Exercise 4**
1 heavily 2 badly 3 dangerous 4 nice
5 slowly 6 clear 7 clearly 8 good
9 heavy 10 easy 11 nicely 12 easily
13 well 14 quickly 15 beautiful
**Exercise 5**
1 He closed the window quietly.
2 She opened the door slowly.
3 She read the newspaper quickly.
4 They speak English well.
5 My uncle sings badly.
6 They work hard.
7 They wrote the postcards quickly.
8 She paints beautifully.
9 He ate the biscuits noisily.
10 They wash their new car very
carefully.
**UNIT 36**
**Exercise 1**
1 I am never late.
2 The bus is often early.
3 My computer is never wrong.
4 It is usually cold here in winter.
5 The fruit in that supermarket is
always fresh.
6 His room is always untidy.
**Exercise 2**
1 You must never hit my dog!

2 He has never played golf.
3 I have never eaten Indian food.
4 He will always love you.
5 I have often swum in the Atlantic.
6 I have never seen snow.
7 You must never tell a lie.
8 You must always tell the truth.
**Exercise 3**
1 He always plays the piano after lunch.
2 I never watch TV in the afternoon.
3 I never put sugar in my tea.
4 I often think about you.
5 We normally start work at 8.30.
6 We always have breakfast in the kitchen.
**Exercise 4**
1 Has he ever worked in France?
2 Have they ever been to Singapore?
3 Have you always driven German cars?
4 Have you ever built a snowman?
5 Has she always lived in a house?
6 Have they always eaten brown bread?
7 Have you ever flown above a mountain?
8 Have you ever been to Africa?
9 Has she ever been to Asia?
10 Have you always had short hair?
**Exercise 5**
1 Does she always take the same bus to work?
2 Do you ever see Tom?
3 Does she ever listen to the radio in her car?
4 Does he ever go to the cinema?
5 Do you always tell the truth?
6 Do you ever lie?
7 Do you sometimes eat biscuits in bed?
8 Do you normally get up at 7 o'clock?
9 Does he often go to bed after midnight?
10 Do you ever drink cold tea on a hot day?
**Exercise 6**
2 She never talks to anyone in the afternoon.
3 She usually wears a hat in bed.
4 She sometimes sleeps in the garden.
5 She has never used a telephone.

6 She has never eaten meat.
7 She never watches TV.
8 In the winter she always wears a T-shirt.
9 In the summer she usually wears three jumpers and a coat.
10 She has never lied to people.
11 She has always told the truth.
12 She usually gives bird food to her cat and cat food to her bird.
13 She normally wears one red shoe and one blue shoe.
14 She has often sung Italian songs on the bus.
15 She always gives money to people who live on the street.
16 She is always kind to me.
17 She has never forgotten my birthday.
18 She usually gives me two presents – £100 and a potato.
19 I always spend the money on her pets.
20 I always give bird food to her bird and cat food to her cat.
21 Her pets are always happy when it's my birthday.
**UNIT 37**
**Exercise 1**
1 on 2 on 3 on 4 at 5 at, at 6 at, in 7 at, on 8 in 9 on 10 in 11 in 12 at 13 on, in 14 at 15 at
**Exercise 2**
1 in 2 at 3 on 4 at 5 in 6 at 7 on 8 in, in 9 at 10 on 11 at, in 12 at 13 at 14 at 15 in
**Exercise 3**
1 in 2 at 3 at 4 in 5 at 6 from, in, to, at 7 from, to, at 8 at 9 from, to, in 10 at, on 11 at, in 12 on, at, in, at, in 13 In, from, to 14 in 15 at 16 in 17 at, on 18 on 19 from, to 20 at
**Exercise 4**
1 On 2 on 3 in 4 in 5 in 6 at 7 in 8 in 9 in 10 in 11 at 12 at 13 at
**Exercise 5**
1 from, to 2 at 3 on 4 at 5 at, on 6 in 7 on 8 In 9 from, to 10 at
**UNIT 38**
**Exercise 1**
2 in 3 next to 4 in front of 5 under 6 behind 7 near 8 opposite 9 above 10 by
**Exercise 2**
1 in 2 at 3 at, at 4 on 5 on 6 on 7 at 8 on 9 on, to 10 at 11 in, in 12 at 13 at

14 in 15 at, in 16 at, in
**Exercise 3**
2 into 3 out of 4 into 5 across 6 out of 7 through 8 to 9 above 10 up 11 out of 12 down 13 up 14 along 15 above 16 out of 17 towards 18 behind 19 above
**UNIT 39**
**Exercise 1**
1 but 2 and 3 and 4 and 5 but 6 and 7 but 8 but 9 but 10 and
**Exercise 2**
2 (h) and 3 (g) but 4 (a) but 5 (d) but 6 (e) and 7 (c) but 8 (b) and 9 (f) and
**UNIT 40**
**Exercise 1**
1 It's either Jackie or Jenny.
2 He's either a dentist or a teacher.
3 We can have either fish or spaghetti.
4 It's either Monday or Tuesday.
5 It's either Washington or New York.
6 It's either a fruit or a vegetable..
7 It's either tea or coffee.
8 There are either 28 or 29.
9 It's either 8.30 or 9.30.
10 It'll be either June or July.
**Exercise 2**
1 Neither Jim nor Vivienne can swim.
2 Neither my aunt nor my uncle can speak Italian.
3 Neither Carol nor William likes music.
4 Neither Laura nor Nicholas watches much television.
5 Neither Ken nor Theresa drinks tea.
6 Neither Tim nor Tina works on Sundays.
7 Neither Tony nor Sarah likes chocolate.
8 Neither Chris nor Francesca listens to the radio.
9 Neither Jenny nor Tom can type.
10 Neither Robert nor Patricia can ride a bicycle.
**UNIT 41**
**Exercise 1**
1 He wanted more money so he changed his job.
2 She wanted to pass her exams so she worked hard.
3 They were very hot so they swam in the river.

4 Jane was hungry so she ordered a large dinner.
5 I like that film very much so I've seen it five times.
**Exercise 2**
1 He got an evening job because he needed more money.
2 He often buys potatoes at the market because he loves chips.
3 She trained every day because she wanted to win the race.
4 He took a photograph because the view was very beautiful.
5 He stood at the back of the group because he was very tall.
**Exercise 3**
1 so 2 because 3 so 4 because 5 because 6 so 7 so 8 because 9 because 10 so
**Exercise 4**
1 (e) so 2 (d) because 3 (i) so 4 (h) so 5 (f) so 6 (g) because 7 (b) because 8 (a) because 9 (c) because
**REVISION TEST 4**
**Units 32-34**
1 B 2 C 3 A 4 B 5 C 6 C 7 B 8 C 9 A 10 B
**Units 35-36**
11 B 12 A 13 C 14 B 15 A 16 C 17 C 18 A 19 B
**Units 37-39**
20 C 21 A 22 B 23 A 24 A 25 A 26 C 27 C 28 A 29 C
**Units 40-41**
30 B 31 C 32 A 33 C 34 A 35 A
**EXIT TEST**
**Units 1-5**
1 B 2 A 3 C 4 A 5 A 6 C
**Units 6-10**
7 B 8 A 9 B 10 C 11 C 12 A 13 B 14 B 15 B 16 C 17 A
**Units 11-15**
18 C 19 B 20 C 21 A 22 A 23 B
**Units 16-21**
24 C 25 B 26 A 27 C 28 C 29 B 30 A 31 A
**Units 22-23**
32 B 33 C 34 C
**Units 24-31**
35 B 36 A 37 C 38 A 39 C 40 C 41 A 42 A 43 C 44 C
**Units 32-41**
45 C 46 B 47 A 48 B 49 C 50 B

## 3 Match the statements and questions

*Match the statements and questions. The first one has been done for you.*

| | |
|---|---|
| 1 We want to sing some songs. | a) Can it take good pictures? |
| 2 Your dog has fallen in the water. | b) Can you cook Italian food? |
| 3 I love spaghetti. | c) Can you dry them? |
| 4 I want to sell my car. | d) Can you speak Spanish? |
| 5 My penfriend lives in Argentina. She's written me a letter. But I can't understand it. | e) Can you drive? |
| 6 That camera is really small. | f) Can it swim? |
| 7 I need some help in the office. | g) Can you post it for me? |
| 8 I've written a letter to Tom. | h) Can you type? |
| 9 I've washed the | i) Can you play the |

## 4 Make questions and answers

*Make questions and give short answers.*
**Examples:**
ski / you / can?
*Can you ski?*
No, I ....
No, I *can't.*

| | |
|---|---|
| 1 waterski / can / you? | Yes, I .... |
| 2 drive a bus / you / can? | No, I .... |
| 3 read Arabic / can / your sister? | Yes, she .... |
| 4 remember / you / his telephone number can? | No, I .... |
| 5 remember / you / his address / can? | No, I .... |
| 6 sleep / you / can / with the light on? | Yes, I .... |
| 7 sleep / you / can / with the window open? | Yes, I .... |
| 8 your parents / play golf / can? | No, they .... |
| 9 your cat / jump / from tree to tree / can? | Yes, it .... |

| | |
|---|---|
| 10 climb a tree / can / you? | No, I .... |
| 11 your keys / find / you / can? | No, I .... |
| 12 she / can / the piano / play? | No, she .... |
| 13 twelve hours a day / you / work / can? | Yes, I .... |
| 14 see / your father / can / without glasses? | No, he .... |
| 15 very fast/ run / can / your dog? | Yes, it .... |

## 5 Complete the story

*Complete the story with* can *or* can't. *The first one has been done for you.*

There is a man in the desert. He's thirsty and tired. The sun is high in the sky. It's 56°C and the man needs water.

Suddenly he sees a tall woman. The woman is carrying a table. On the table there are three ties.

The man goes to the woman and says '**(1)** *Can* you help me? I need water. I **(2)** .... live without water!'

'I'm sorry,' the woman says. 'I **(3)** .... help you. I don't have any water. But I **(4)** .... sell you a tie. I have three ties. You **(5)** .... have a yellow one, a blue one or a red one.

'I don't want a tie,' the man says. 'I need water. Can't you understand that?' He walks away. It is now 58°C.

An hour later the man sees a young boy. The boy is carrying a table. On the table there are three ties.

The man goes to the boy and says, '**(6)** .... you help me? I need water. I **(7)** .... live without water.'

'I'm sorry,' the young boy says. 'I **(8)** .... help you. I have no water. But I **(9)** .... sell you a tie. I have three ties. You **(10)** .... buy a brown one, a green one or an orange one.'

'I don't need a tie,' the man says. 'I need water. Can't you understand that?' He walks away. It is now 60°C.

Many hours later, the man arrives at a hotel. 'Ah,' he thinks. 'A hotel! I **(11)** .... find water there.'

The doorman looks at him and says, '**(12)** .... I help you, sir?'

'Water!' the man says. 'Let me go into the hotel. I need water.'

'I'm sorry, sir,' the doorman says. 'But this is a very expensive hotel. And you **(13)** .... come in here without a tie.'

# Asking Questions 1: *What / When / Where / Which / Why / How / How many / How much*

## FORM

We often make questions with *What, When, Where, Which, How, How many* and *How much*.
There are three important forms.
**1** Question word + *to be* (*am / is / are / was / were*) + subject
*What is* your name?
*When is* your birthday?
*Where are* my shoes?
*How are* you?
*Where were* the 1992 Olympics?
**2** Question word + auxiliary / modal + subject + base verb

*What did* you do yesterday?
*When will* the train arrive?
*Where can* I buy petrol?
*How do* you spell 'potato'?
**3** *What / Which / How many* + object + auxiliary / modal + subject + base verb
*What* shampoo *do you* use?
*Which* jumper *did* you wear – the red one or the blue one?
*How many* eggs *do* you have for breakfast?
*How many* eggs *can* you eat?

## USE

We use
**1** *When* to ask about days, dates and times
*When is the match? It's on Saturday at 3 o'clock.*
*When are we going to Jamaica? On 21st July.*
**2** *Where* to ask about places
*Where is the post office?*
*Where do you live?*
**3** *Why* to ask about reasons
*Why do dogs have tails?*
*Why are you going out?*
**4** We normally answer *How* + adjective and *How* + adverb questions with a number, an adjective or an adverb
*How **old** is she?*
***Twelve**. She's very **young**.*
*How **fast** do you drive?*
***Twenty** kilometres an hour. Very **slowly**!*
**5** We use *How many* + the plural form of a countable noun, and *How much* + an uncountable noun.
*How many sisters do you have?*
*How much petrol do we need?*

**6** Be careful with *What*.
Look at these two questions.
*What **is** the capital of New Zealand?*
*What **do you want** for your birthday?*
We normally use *What + to be* when there is only one possible answer *(The capital of New Zealand is Auckland)*.
We normally use *What* + auxiliary + subject + base verb when there are many possible answers *(I want a bicycle / a book / some oranges / biscuits / money ...)*.
**7** Be careful with *Which*.
Look at these sentences.
*You can have **white bread** or **brown bread**. **Which do you prefer?***
*There's **apple juice, orange juice** and **lemonade** in the fridge. **Which one do you want?***
We normally use *Which* + auxiliary + subject + base verb or *Which* + object + auxiliary + subject + base verb when there are only two or three possible answers.

### 1 Make questions

*Make questions with* What, When *or* Where.
**Example:**
*What* time did you get up yesterday?
1 .......... does your aunt live? In a small flat near the market.
2 .......... are you doing tomorrow? I'm playing basketball.
3 .......... is the capital of Australia? Canberra, I think.
4 .......... is your bicycle? I left it in the street.
5 .......... does the train leave? At 3 o'clock in the afternoon.
6 .......... did you meet Jenny? In 1997.
7 .......... is your favourite colour? Blue.
8 .......... is a parrot? It's a bird.

### 2 Complete the sentences

*Complete the sentences with* How much *or* How many.
*The first one has been done for you.*

| | |
|---|---|
| **1** *How many* brothers have you got? | Five. We're a big family. |
| **2** .......... people know this secret? | Just two. You and me. |
| **3** .......... petrol do we need? | Not much, two or three litres. |
| **4** .......... cups do we need? | One for you, one for me! |
| **5** .......... water shall we add? | Just a little. |
| **6** .......... snow fell yesterday? | About 10 centimetres. |
| **7** .......... lessons do we have today? | Just one. |
| **8** .......... cups of coffee did he drink? | Twelve! He was thirsty. |

## 3 Complete the dialogues

*Your sister went to a party last night. You are asking her some questions. Complete the dialogues with* What, When, Where *or* How many *and a past simple verb.*

**Example:**
you go / last night?
*Where did you go last night?*
I went to Sally's birthday party.

**1** .......... you wear?
I wore my blue dress.
**2** .......... you arrive?
At about 8.30.
**3** .......... you eat?
There wasn't much food! I ate a lot of small cakes.
**4** .......... you eat?
About twenty. They were delicious!
**5** .......... James arrive?
He arrived at about 9.00.
**6** .......... you sit?
We sat in the garden and talked. It was really nice!
**7** .......... you give Sally for her birthday?
I gave her a camera. She took some photographs.
**8** .......... she take?
About thirty. She took five of James and me!

## 4 Make questions

*Make questions from the* underlined *words. Use* Which.

**Example:**
soft drink / you / prefer, Pepsi or Coca Cola?
*Which soft drink do you prefer, Pepsi or Coca Cola?*

**1** dress / you / prefer, the yellow one or the blue one?
**2** apple / you / want, the big one or the small one?
**3** drink / you / prefer, tea or coffee?
**4** bus / you / take to work, the number 24 or the number 40?
**5** city / you prefer, Hong Kong or Beijing?

## 5 Put the words in the right order

*Put the* underlined *words in the right order to make sentences.*

**Example:**
film / shall / see / we / which, 'Love Story' or 'The Train to Istanbul'?
*Which film shall we see, 'Love Story' or 'The Train to Istanbul'?*

**1** flour / which / you / buy / did, the white or the brown?
**2** restaurant / we / go to / shall / which, The Rice Garden or Pizza Now?
**3** pencil / can / which / use / I, this one or that one?
**4** room / paint / they / which / did, the bedroom or the kitchen?
**5** which / we / road / take / shall, the left or the right?

## 6 Make questions

*Make questions. Use* How *and an adjective or adverb from the box.*

| far(x2) | fast | long | often(x2) | old | tall |
|---|---|---|---|---|---|

**Example:**
*How often* do they play golf?
They play three times a week.
**1** .......... is the River Nile?
About 3,000 kilometres.
**2** .......... is Mr Thompson?
He's 1.72.
**3** .......... do you see your brother?
Three or four times a week.
**4** .......... is your nephew?
He's seven.
**5** .......... does she drive?
About 200 kilometres an hour!
**6** .......... is it from here to Manchester?
About twelve kilometres.
**7** .......... do you eat potatoes?
Every day. I love chips.
**8** .......... is it from here to the post office?
It's not far. Go to the traffic lights and turn right.

# UNIT 23 Asking Questions 2: *Who*
## Who does Tim love? or Who loves Tim?

## FORM

**1** Look at these examples:
a) *Who **told** Tom?*
b) *Who **did** Tom tell?*
These are questions with *Who*.
**2** We make questions with *Who* in two different ways.
**A** When *Who* is the subject.
*Who loves Tim?*
*Who broke the window?*
*Who has taken my book?*
*Who can climb that wall?*
In these examples, *Tim, the window, my book* and *that wall* are the objects of their sentences.
**B** When *Who* is the object.
*Who does Tim love?*
*Who did the dog frighten?*
*Who has Mary kissed?*
*Who must Roger thank?*

In these examples, *Tim, the dog, Mary* and *Roger* are the subjects of their sentences.
In a), the form is *Who* + verb + object.
In b), the form is *Who* + auxiliary / modal + subject + verb
**3** Some verbs are often followed by a preposition
*talk to – John's **talking to** Ros.*
*Write to – Mary has **written** a letter **to** Jack.*
*Work with – Kate **works with** Richard.*
When the preposition is followed by a person's name or a description of a person, then we can begin the question *Who* and end with the preposition.
***Who** is John talking **to**?*
***Who** has Mary written **to**?*
***Who** does Kate work **with**?*
In these cases the form is
*Who* + auxiliary / modal + subject + verb + preposition

## 1 Make questions

*Put the words in the right order to make questions.*
**Example:**
my apple / ate / who?
*Who ate my apple?*

1 who / talking to / are you?
2 who / going to the cinema with / are you?
3 telephoned / who / Fred?
4 did / who / Fred telephone?
5 who / Francesca / wrote to?
6 who / Francesca / write to / did?
7 played / tennis / who?
8 who / play tennis with / you / did?
9 did / to the party / invite / who / you?
10 who / to the party / invited you?

## 2 Read and write questions

*Read the story. After the story there are some answers to questions about the story. Write the question for each answer. The first two have been done for you.*

In the middle of Buenos Aires, Antonio is watching a football match on television. His favourite team is playing. It's an important game. Suddenly, Antonio's team gets a goal. His team has won 3–2.
Antonio kisses Julietta, his wife. She kisses Alberto, their baby son. Alberto laughs at Antonio.

Carlos, his uncle, has also watched the game. He telephoned his friend, Juan. Juan tells his wife, Lita. Then Lita told her friend Carmen. Carmen's mother was cooking the dinner. Carmen's husband, Paulo was very excited.
Paulo ran to tell his friend Marco. Marco wasn't interested. He was having a quarrel with his wife, Maria. She forgot to tell him about the game!

1 *Who laughs?* Alberto,
2 *Who does Antonio kiss?* Julietta.
3 ..........................Antonio.
4 ..........................Carlos.
5 ..........................Juan.
6 ..........................Lita.
7 ..........................Carmen.
8 ..........................Carmen's mother.
9 ..........................Paulo.
10 ..........................Marco.
11 ..........................Marco and his wife, Maria.
12 ..........................Maria.

# UNITS 11-23  Unit Revision Test 2

*The questions in Revision Test 2 are about the grammar in Units 11–23. Choose the best answer, A, B or C.*

## UNITS 11-14

**1** Don't .... that!
A do  B to do  C doing

**2** Open .... .
A please the bag  B the bag please  C you please the bag

**3** The photographs .... beautiful.
A were  B was  C they

**4** He .... at home yesterday.
A were  B was  C weren't

**5** When .... in Portugal?
A were they  B was they  C they were

**6** I .... her in 1997.
A have met  B was met  C met

**7** The baby .... all day.
A it cried  B cried  C cryed

**8** They .... the house in 1995.
A not buy  B not bought  C didn't buy

**9** .... last night?
A Did it rain  B Did it to rain  C Did it rains

**10** .... Mr Rolls and Mr Royce build their first car in 1906?
A Have  B Does  C Did

**11** Did you eat those biscuits? Yes, I .... .
A did  B didn't  C do

## UNITS 15-17

**12** Jane .... in the bath when the telephone rang.
A sitting  B was sitting  C is sitting

**13** .... when you arrived?
A Eating they were  B Were they eating  C Eating they

**14** Vivienne was studying at university when she .... Jim.
A met  B has met  C is meeting

**15** He .... his hair. It's still wet.
A has wash  B washing  C has washed

**16** .... your shoes?
A Have you to clean  B Has you cleaned  C Have you cleaned

**17** I have .... the newspaper.
A buyed  B buying  C bought

**18** They .... to Manchester. They're coming back on Monday.
A have been  B have gone  C have go

**19** .... Tom arrived?
A Is  B Have  C Has

**20** Have you spoken to Harry? No, I .... .
A haven't  B have  C hasn't

**21** Have you ....?
A Chinese food eaten ever  B ever eaten Chinese food  C Chinese food ever eaten

**22** No, I've .... Chinese food.
A never ate  B eaten never  C never eaten

## UNITS 18-19

**23** I .... buy a new jumper tomorrow.
A am going to  B am going  C going to

**24** She's going .... a shower
A to having  B to have  C have

**25** Am .... be rich?
A I going to  B he going to  C they going to

**26** .... see you next week.
A I'll to  B I'll  C I going to

**27** They .... play football tomorrow
A won't  B will to  C won't to

**28** It's snowing! ....?
A Shall we a taxi take  B Will we a taxi take  C Shall we take a taxi

## UNITS 20-23

**29** You .... lie to me. Tell the truth.
A mustn't to  B haven't  C mustn't

**30** You .... pay to go into the museum. It's free.
A mustn't  B doesn't have to  C don't have to

**31** .... to eat all these vegetables?
A Must I  B Do I have  C Does I have

**32** Jackie .... swim.
A can't  B can't to  C don't

**33** Can you play the piano? Yes, I ....
A can  B can't  C doesn't

**34** Where ....?
A the post office is  B be the post office  C is the post office

**35** We have white bread and brown bread. .... do you prefer?
A Which  B When  C What

**36** .... do you want for your birthday?
A Which  B When  C What

# UNIT 24 Articles 1: a / an
## an apple; a bicycle
## FORM AND USE

We use *a* or *an* to talk about one of something.
*Tom ate **an** apple.*
**1** Put *an* before a vowel (a, e, i, o, u)
*an apple, an egg, an Indian restaurant, an orange, an umbrella*
**2** Put *a* before a consonant (the other 21 letters of the alphabet)
*a bicycle, a cat, a garden, a red train, a zoo*
**But:**
**3** Use *an* in front of *hour*
*They talked for **an hour**.*
Use *a* in front of *eu*
*Paris is **a European** city.*

Use *a* in front of *u* if you hear *yoo*
*Is there **a university** in this city?*
Use *an* in front of *h* if the *h* is silent
*Everyone knows that Tom is **an honest** man.*
**4** We use *a* and *an* with the name of a job
*I'm **a** writer. She's **a** teacher. He's **an** artist.*
**5** *a* and *an* often mean *every*
*I work for eight hours a day. (= I work for eight hours every day.)*
*The apples are $1.00 a kilo.*
*The aeroplane flies at 900 kilometres an hour.*

### 1 Write *a* or *an*

1 *a* car
2 .......... orange car
3 .......... dog
4 .......... big dog
5 .......... aeroplane
6 .......... Italian aeroplane
7 .......... small Italian aeroplane
8 .......... question
9 .......... important question
10 .......... tree near the river
11 .......... room in your school
12 .......... yellow window in a green kitchen
13 .......... elephant in a zoo
14 .......... European country
15 .......... egg on .......... plate
16 .......... fried egg
17 .......... green field
18 .......... field
19 .......... apple
20 .......... fresh apple

### 2 Complete the sentences

*Complete the sentences with* a *or* an. *The first one has been done for you.*

1 I worked for *an* hour and *a* half and then fell asleep.
2 There's ....... dog in the garden.
3 The shop is open for ten hours ....... day.
4 I need ....... holiday!
5 Do you want ....... ice-cream?

6 Olivetti is ...... Italian company.
7 That's ...... interesting question!
8 I watched ...... French film on TV yesterday. It was about ...... man and ...... woman who loved the sea. They bought ...... old boat and went around the world.
9 I always eat ...... orange before I go to bed.
10 They have ...... office in the centre of the city.
11 The train goes at 250km ...... hour.
12 We paid $20 ...... night for the hotel.
13 We have ...... cup of coffee every morning.
14 The circus bought ...... new elephant.
15 I watched television for ...... hour, then went to bed.
16 She has unusual pets, ..... snake and ...... hen!
17 I'm taking ..... week off work.
18 My mother is ..... doctor, and my father is ..... actor.
19 He didn't read ...... magazine, he read ..... book.
20 She had ..... egg and ..... glass of milk for breakfast.

### 3 Make sentences

*Put the words in the right order to make sentences.*
**Example:**
the cinema / go to / we / once / month / a
*We go to the cinema once a month.*

1 has/ he / a / a birthday / party / year / once
2 a / train / to Tokyo / an / three times / there is / hour
3 watches / he / television / five hours / day / a

50

4 she / her brother / month / telephones / a / three or four times

5 they / twice / year / to Spain / a / go

6 We / four times / week / study / a / English

7 driving / 225 / an / he was / at / hour / kilometres

8 my uncle / 12 hours / day / a / works

9 30 kilometres / the balloon / an / flies / hour / at

10 we / for the tomatoes / $3 / kilo / a / paid

11 a / we/ fish / eat / once / week

12 television / that  programme / is / on / a / twice / day

13 once / his mother / a / phones / day / he

14 on holiday / a / they / three times / go / year

15 spend / a / we / sleeping / third of our lives

### 4 | Complete the dialogue

*It's your birthday. Your brother Fred has made you a special meal. Complete the dialogue with* a *or* an. *The first one has been done for you.*

**You:** Fred, what is this?

**Fred:** It's **(1)** *a* fruit salad. I got **(2)** .......... book from the library and in the book there was **(3)** .......... page about how to make **(4)** .......... fruit salad.

**You:** And what did the book say, Fred?

**Fred:** Well, the book said: 'To make a fruit salad you take **(5)** .......... apple, **(6)** .......... orange, **(7)** .......... banana, **(8)** .......... hundred millilitres of milk and **(9)** .......... cup of sugar. You put them all together in **(10)** .......... bowl.' And that's **(11)** .......... fruit salad!

**You:** Well, it's very nice of you but I think it's **(12)** .......... excellent idea if you take the skin off the apple and the orange and the banana first!

### 5 | Complete the dialogue

*Fred is in a pet shop. Complete the dialogue. Write* a *or* an. *The first one has been done for you.*

**Fred:** Good afternoon, I want to buy a wasp, please.

**Mr Jones:** A wasp? I'm sorry, sir. This is a pet shop. We don't sell wasps. You can buy **(1)** *a* cat or **(2)** .......... dog or **(3)** .......... elephant here, but you can't buy a wasp.

**Fred:** Look, I don't want to buy **(4)** .......... fish or **(5)** .......... African lion or **(6)** .......... Chinese giraffe. I want to buy **(7)** .......... wasp, please.

**Mr Jones:** But, sir. We don't sell wasps.

**Fred:** But you've got one in the window!

### 6 | Complete the sentences

*Rearrange the letters in the words below and then use them to complete the gaps in the sentences below. When you complete sentences, put 'a' or 'an' before the word you choose.*

LANIMA  PLPAE  MRA  KNBA  TLTBOE  RCA
OGD  RAE  NEVEOPLE  NNGEEVI  RDAGNE
LIDAHOY  TOIINNTIVA  EMNA  FIFCEO
GREOAN  RTSIH  HEOS  ANITR  LMLABURE

1 He heard .......... bark during the night.

2 She broke .......... when she fell.

3 They found .......... by the lake.

4 I've got .......... to Jack's party.

5 His mother gave him .......... to take to school.

6 They've opened .......... on the corner of the street.

7 Mary drew a man without .......... How could he hear anything?

8 He was a man without .......... Nobody knew who he was.

9 They went on .......... to Spain.

10 Jane eats .......... every day.

11 Could I have .......... of milk, please?

12 The car's broken.  What time is there .......... to London?

13 I can't post the letter.  I haven't got ..........

14 They met on .......... in May when it was getting dark.

15 They've got .......... beautiful .......... with many unusual plants.

16 I can't drive, so I haven't got ..........

17 It's going to rain.  Take .......... !

18 He's gone to buy .......... They're very cheap in that shop.

19 They saw .......... strange .......... in the zoo.

20 She works in .......... in the centre of the town.

# UNIT 25 Articles 2: *the* / no article (Ø)

## USE

**THE**

**1** We use *a* and *an* when we talk about something for the first time. We use *the* when we talk about it for a second time.
*I have **a** cat and **a** dog. **The** cat is black and **the** dog is white*.

**2** We use *the*
**A** for rivers, seas and oceans
*the Amazon, the Red Sea, the Atlantic*
**B** for deserts
*the Sahara, the Gobi, the Kalahari*
**C** for a group of mountains
*the Alps, the Himalayas, the Pyrenees*
**D** for a group of islands
*the West Indies, the Bahamas, the Azores*
**E** when there is only one of something
*the earth, the world, the sun, the moon, the sky*
**F** for rooms in a house
*the kitchen, the bathroom*

**3** We use *play + the* with the name of a musical instrument.
*Do you play **the piano**?*
*She plays **the guitar***.

**NO ARTICLE Ø**

**1** We do not use *the* when we talk about something in a general way.
***Gold** is expensive.*
*I love **music**.*
*Do you like **rice**?*
But we add *the* when we are more specific.
***The gold** you bought yesterday was expensive.*
*I love **the music** of the 1960s.*
*We had a wonderful meal. **The rice** was delicious.*

**2** We do not use *the* for
**A** cities
*I live in Tokyo. They work in Toronto.*
**B** countries
*She is going to Australia.*
*He comes from Singapore.*
**But there are some exceptions:**
*The United States, The United Kingdom, The Philippines*
**C** continents
*Africa, Asia, Europe*
**D** meals
*What time is breakfast?*
*What are we having for dinner?*
**E** sports
*tennis, football, cricket*

## 1 Complete the dialogues

*Complete the sentences with* a, an *or the. The first one has been done for you.*

1 **Jane:** There's *a* postcard and .......... letter for you.
**Charles:** Who are they from?
**Jane:** .......... postcard is from your sister and .......... letter is from your bank.
**Charles:** I think I'll read the postcard now, and I'll read the letter after lunch!

2 **Ken:** We have .......... flat in the city and .......... house in the country.
**Jane:** So where do you live?
**Ken:** Well, during the week we live in .......... flat and at the weekend we live in .......... house.

3 **Andrew:** I have .......... bicycle and .......... car. I use .......... bicycle when I go to work and I use .......... car when I go shopping.
**Patricia:** That's nothing! I have .......... helicopter and .......... aeroplane. I use .......... helicopter to fly around my garden and I use .......... aeroplane when I go to the West Indies on holiday.

## 2 Choose the correct form

*Choose the correct form in brackets and* underline *it.*
**Examples:**
I love this restaurant. (Food / The food) here is very good.
We all need (love / the love).

1 I don't eat (meat / the meat). I'm a vegetarian.
2 I don't feel very well. Was (meat / the meat) we ate yesterday fresh?
3 Do you drink (milk / the milk)?

**4** Where is (milk / the milk) we bought yesterday?

**5** In a desert, (water / the water) is more expensive than (chocolate / the chocolate).

**6** We swam in the sea near Jamaica last month. (Water / The water) there is clear and blue.

**7** What is more important, (love / the love) or (money / the money)?

**8** (Homework / The homework) we did last night was very difficult.

**9** I don't like (cities / the cities). They're too noisy.

**10** (Photographs / The photographs) you took of Singapore are wonderful!

**11** I like (photographs / the photographs) of people more than paintings.

**12** (Coffee / The coffee) I had for breakfast was very good.

**13** She drank all (the coffee / coffee) in the house.

**14** I like (dogs / the dogs). They are very friendly.

**15** I don't need (friends / the friends). I like to be alone.

**16** Where can you park (cars / the cars) in this town?

**17** Do you want (coffee / the coffee), or (juice / the juice) I bought last week?

**18** Shall we buy (blue car / the blue car) or (red car / the red car)?

**19** We cannot live without (water / the water).

**20** I always go to America on holiday. I like (people / the people).

**3** **Complete the sentences**

*Complete the sentences with* the *or* Ø *(no article).*

**Example:**
She plays Ø tennis.
He plays *the* guitar.

**1** .......... Sahara is the biggest desert in Africa.

**2** .......... Buenos Aires is in Argentina.

**3** I love .......... football but I don't understand .......... cricket.

**4** How many people live in .......... India?

**5** .......... Pacific is bigger than .......... Atlantic.

**6** Have you ever been to .......... France?

**7** Have you ever played .......... golf?

**8** Don't look at .......... sun. It's bad for your eyes.

**9** We met in .......... Europe, got married in .......... Africa and now live in .......... Asia.

**10** What are we having for .......... lunch?

**11** I was born in .......... West Indies.

**12** .......... Amazon is the longest river in .......... world.

**13** Washington is ..... capital city of .... USA.

**14** ..... dinner we had yesterday was horrible!

**15** Where is ..... Nile, in ..... Africa or in ..... South America?

**4** **Complete the sentences**

*Complete the sentences with* the *or* Ø *(no article). The first one has been done for you.*

**1** She always plays *the* guitar before breakfast.

**2** I was born in .......... Philippines but I grew up in .......... Australia.

**3** It's a beautiful day. Let's have .......... lunch on the beach!

**4** Have you ever been to .......... Bahamas?

**5** Is .......... football popular in your country?

**6** Jackie's in .......... bathroom. She's having a shower.

**7** I'm reading a book about .......... Himalayas at the moment.

**8** Have you ever swum in .......... Pacific?

**9** .......... sky is dark. I think it's going to rain.

**10** What is the biggest country in .......... Asia?

**11** He lives in a palace in the middle of .......... Sahara.

**12** Does this train go to .......... Amsterdam?

**13** ..... sun is shining. Let's go into ..... garden.

**14** Can you speak .... Turkish?

**15** Is this ..... train for Paris?

**5** **Fill in the gaps**

*Fill in the gaps in the story with* a, an, the *or* Ø*. The first one has been done for you.*

Last week, John caught **(1)** *a* train to **(2)** .......... Paris in **(3)** .......... morning and arrived there at **(4)** .......... midday. He wanted to see **(5)** .......... Eiffel Tower. So he took **(6)** .......... bus. **(7)** .......... bus was very slow and he didn't get to **(8)** .......... tower until three o'clock. At six o'clock, he had to catch **(9)** .......... train back home. He looked at **(10)** .......... map of **(11)** .......... district. He had to walk **(12)** .......... long way from **(13)** .......... bus stop to **(14)** .......... tower. It was very late. So he took **(15)** .......... taxi back to **(16)** .......... station. He never saw the Eiffel Tower.

# UNIT 26 Demonstratives: *this / that, these / those*
## this watch; those birds

## FORM AND USE

**1** Look at these sentences.

*Do you like **this** watch? It's Swiss.*

*Can you see **that** yellow house on the hill? I live there.*

***These** chocolates are wonderful. Have one.*

*Look at **those** birds in the sky. They're going south for the winter.*

We use *this, that, these* and *those* to identify the person or the thing we are talking about.

**Position**

**1** We use *this* and *these* to talk about things or people that are near to us.

this + a singular noun

these + a plural noun

***This** soup is delicious. Try it!*

***These** shoes are dirty. I must clean them.*

**2** We use *that* and *those* to talk about things or people that are more distant from us.

that + a singular noun

those + a plural noun

***That** plane is flying to Japan.*

***Those** mountains are 10 kilometres away.*

**Time**

**1** We use *this* for time that is near to us (usually in the present or near future).

*What are you doing **this** evening?*

**2** We use *that* for time that is far from us (usually in the past).

*He started university in 1995. He bought his first bicycle **that** year.*

**People**

**1** We use *this* and *these* to introduce people.

***This** is Jane. She's my best friend.*

***These** are my cousins, Jim and David.*

**2** On the telephone, we use *is that* and *this is*.

***Is that** the police station? I've lost my cat.*

*(Is that = Am I talking to ...?)*

***This is** Tim Roberts. Can I speak to Mr Edison, please?*

*(This is = My name is ... )*

## 1 Complete the instructions

*Fred is helping Jackie to move into her new flat. Complete Jackie's instructions to Fred with* this, that, these *or* those. *The first one has been done for you.*

OK, Fred, can you put (**1**) *this* chair here next to (**2**) .......... table there. No, that's not right! Put (**3**) .......... chair here next to (**4**) .......... desk there. Yes, that's better. Now, put (**5**) .......... books here on (**6**) .......... table there and put (**7**) .......... cups there on (**8**) .......... shelf there. Good. Now, can you put (**9**) .......... magazines here on (**10**) .......... armchair there and put (**11**) .......... cushions there on (**12**) .......... sofa here. No, no – that's not right. Put (**13**) .......... cushions there on (**14**) .......... armchair here and put (**15**) .......... glasses here on (**16**) .......... table there. No, Fred, you can't sit down on (**17**) .......... sofa there. I know you're tired but you can't go to sleep on (**18**) .......... cushions there. Fred! Hey, wake up!

## 2 Complete the sentences

*Complete the sentences with* this *or* these.

**Example:**

Does *this* train go to Glasgow?

**1** We're on holiday .......... week, so we've rented a car.

**2** .......... is my brother, Tim and .......... are my sisters, Jenny and Teresa.

**3** Please help me. .......... bags are very heavy.

**4** Where are you going .......... afternoon?

**5** Is .......... seat free?
Yes, it is.

**6** Can I use .......... pen here?

**7** I'm very hungry. Can I have .......... biscuits?

**8** How much is .......... magazine?

**9** Hello. .......... is Sally. Can I speak to Tina, please?

**10** I can't walk very fast. .......... shoes are new!

**11** I think ..... trousers fit me very well.

**12** Is ..... bus going into town?

**13** I must stand up, ..... seat is very hard.

**14** ..... ice-cream is very good. Do you want some?

**15** Where do .... magazines go?

**16** Do you like .... film?

**17** ..... are my dogs, Tom and Jerry.

**18** Are ..... gloves yours or mine?

**19** ..... children should be in school.

**20** Here we are, ..... is my new flat.

## 3 Complete the sentences

*Complete the sentences with* that *or* those.
**Example:**
*That* shampoo is very expensive.

1 Can you pass me .......... books, please?
2 Where did you buy .......... dress? It's beautiful.
3 Look at .......... cows. They're sitting down. I think it's going to rain.
4 Can I use .......... pencil there?
5 Don't eat .......... bananas. They're green.
6 It was my birthday yesterday. We went to .......... new Italian restaurant near the station.
7 We moved to Australia in 1992. I saw my first game of cricket .......... year.
8 .......... cakes were delicious! I've eaten them all!
9 Hello. Is .......... the library?
10 Who are .......... people over there?
11 I'll have .......... apples, please. They look delicious.
12 Did you remember to bring .......... book I want?
13 Have you seen .......... film yet?
14 Where are .......... new shoes you bought?
15 .......... coffee is very expensive, but .......... tea-bags are cheap.
16 Look at .......... man. I think he's ill. Let's help him.
17 Is .......... the station over there?
18 Where are .......... tickets. I put them in the drawer yesterday.
19 Are .......... sandwiches ready, yet?
20 .......... is her mother, and .......... are her sisters.

## 4 Complete Hannah's answers

*Mary is on a train with Hannah, a young French girl. The train has stopped. Mary is encouraging Hannah to practise her English. The things in the train are near to her, and those outside are distant. Complete Hannah's answers with* this, that, these *or* those. *The first one has been done for you.*

**Mary:** Now, Hannah, give me the English names for these things.
**Hannah:** **(1)** *This* is *a table*.
**(2)** .......... is ..........
**(3)** .......... is ..........
**(4)** .......... is ..........
**(5)** .......... is ..........
**(6)** .......... are ..........
**(7)** .......... are ..........
**(8)** .......... is ..........
**(9)** .......... is ..........
**(10)** .......... is ..........
**(11)** .......... is ..........
**(12)** .......... are ..........
**(13)** .......... are ..........
**Mary:** Very good, Hannah!

# Pronouns: Subject and Object
## He likes it

## FORM AND USE

### SUBJECT AND OBJECT

Look at these sentences.

| Subject | + | Verb | + | Object |
|---|---|---|---|---|
| Fred | | likes | | chocolate. |
| *He* | | *likes* | | *it*. |
| Paul and Tina | | love | | their children. |
| *They* | | *love* | | *them*. |

Many sentences in English are like this. They have a subject, a verb and an object.

In the examples above, the subject can be a noun (*Fred, Paul* and *Tina*) or a pronoun (*he, they*).

The object can be a noun (*chocolate, their children*) or a pronoun (*it, them*).

### NOUN OR PRONOUN?

**Subject**

Look at these sentences.

(a) *My sister* is very tall. *My sister* plays a lot of basketball.

(b) *My sister* is very tall. *She* plays a lot of basketball.

In the second sentence (b), we replace the subject (*My sister*) with a subject pronoun (*She*). We do this in writing and conversation.

**Object**

Look at these sentences.

(a) *I saw this new camera. I bought the camera.*

(b) *I saw this new camera. I bought it.*

In the second sentence (b), we replace the object (*the camera*) with an object pronoun (*it*). We do this in writing and in conversation.

### SUBJECT AND OBJECT PRONOUNS

| Subject pronouns | Object pronouns |
|---|---|
| I | me |
| you | you |
| he | him |
| she | her |
| it | it |
| we | us |
| they | them |

*I* met **her** in 1995.

*They* sent **us** a postcard from Australia.

*He* phoned **me** yesterday.

*We* have known **her** for twenty years.

*We* saw **them** in the park.

**Note:**

We often use the subject pronoun *it* when we talk about the time, the date, the day, the weather, an animal, things we study and measurements (like centimetres and kilometres).

*It's* 6 o'clock.

*It's* 3rd June.

*It's Saturday*. *I'm not working today.*

*It's* cold in here.

*I have a cat. **It's** three months old.*

*I'm learning German. **It's** a difficult language!*

*It's* 3500 kilometres from here to Tokyo.

---

### 1 Replace the word

*Replace the underlined word or words with a subject pronoun,* he, she, it, we *or* they.

**Example:**

Fred and I love music. Fred and I often go to concerts.

*Fred and I love music. **We** often go to concerts.*

1 The book is very long. <u>The book</u> has 315 pages.
2 My sister is very rich. <u>My sister</u> has four houses.
3 Sally and I are learning Spanish. <u>Sally and I</u> study three hours a day.
4 Sally and I are learning Spanish. <u>Spanish</u> is a beautiful language.
5 My uncle is a builder. <u>My uncle</u> works very hard.
6 Paris is very near here. <u>Paris</u> is about 10 kilometres away.
7 Fred and Sally hate flying. <u>Fred and Sally</u> never go by plane.

8 The shop is open six days a week. <u>The shop</u> is closed on Sundays.
9 Richard and Sam are playing tennis. <u>Richard and Sam</u> play every Saturday.
10 My aunt is a doctor. <u>My aunt</u> often works at night.
11 This bread is wonderful! <u>The bread</u> is very fresh.
12 The bus is full. <u>The bus</u> is always full at this time of day.
13 Mike and Anna love cold weather. <u>Mike and Anna</u> are going to Greenland on holiday this year.
14 My cat is very lazy. <u>My cat</u> sleeps all day.

### 2 Replace the word

*Replace the underlined word or words with an object pronoun,* him, her, it, us *or* them.

**Example:**

I love television. I watch <u>television</u> five hours a day.

*I love television. I watch **it** five hours a day.*

1 Jenny has four dogs. She takes <u>the dogs</u> to the park every day.
2 I have a new bicycle. I bought <u>the bicycle</u> yesterday.
3 I spoke to your aunt today. I met <u>your aunt</u> at the supermarket.
4 I spoke to your brothers today. I met <u>your brothers</u> at the post office.
5 Nicola speaks Arabic. She learned <u>Arabic</u> at school.
6 I listen to the radio every day. I listen to <u>the radio</u> in my car.
7 Jim sent Jackie and me a postcard from Hawaii. He told <u>Jackie and me</u> it was 39°C there. Very hot!
8 Jackie and I sent Jim a postcard from London. We told <u>Jim</u> it was 3°C and snowing. Very cold!
9 She made some tea. I drank <u>the tea</u>.
10 She made some biscuits. I ate <u>the biscuits</u>.
11 She made a lot of money. I spent <u>the money</u>.
12 These shoes are dirty. I must clean <u>the shoes</u>.
13 This question is very difficult. I don't understand <u>this question</u>.
14 I love that dress. Where did you buy <u>that dress</u>?

<h3>3  What happens next?</h3>

*Your sister has just had a baby. She phones your mother and father to tell them the news. Use subject pronouns to explain what happens next. The first two have been done for you.*

They brought the telephone to my sister. (1) *She* phoned my mother and father. (2) *They* phoned Uncle Bert. (3) .......... phoned Carol and Nancy. (4) .......... phoned Tom. (5) .......... phoned Aunt Beryl. (6) .......... phoned Aunt Vera. (7) .......... phoned my grandparents. (8) .......... phoned Uncle James. (9) .......... phoned our cousins. (10) .......... phoned Bill. (11) .......... phoned Jackie and me. (12) .......... phoned my sister.

<h3>4  Make sentences</h3>

*Put the <u>underlined</u> words in the right order to make sentences.*
**Example:**
Mike's got a new car. <u>bought / it / he / yesterday</u>
*Mike's got a new car. He bought it yesterday.*

1 Paul and I love spaghetti. <u>food / Italian / eat / we / often</u>
2 Paul and Mark love Japanese food. <u>often eat / sushi / they</u>
3 This tea is very hot! <u>drink / I / it / can't</u>
4 My sister saw a French film at the cinema. <u>it / loved / she</u>
5 Fred and I wrote to Father Christmas. <u>him / every year / write to / we</u>
6 Father Christmas brought Fred and me a present. <u>a / present every year / brings / he / us</u>
7 Uncle James is coming to dinner. <u>at the station / we / him / are meeting</u>
8 She has written some beautiful songs. <u>played / them / she / to us yesterday</u>

<h3>5  Complete this interview</h3>

*Ted Turner lives in Mates Road. He helps his neighbours and they help him. He is talking on the radio about Mates Road. Complete the interview with subject and object pronouns. The first four have been done for you.*

**Interviewer:** Mr Turner. Tell us about your neighbours.
**Mr Turner:** Well, Mr Evans lives at number 23. He doesn't have a car but he has a big garden. So, (1) *I* drive (2) *him* to work and (3) *he* gives (4) *me* fresh apples from his trees.

Mrs Velasquez lives at number 25. She doesn't speak English and I don't speak Spanish. So, (5) .......... teach (6) .......... English and (7) .......... teaches (8) .......... Spanish.

Mr and Mrs Cornwall are at number 27. They don't like cooking and I don't like washing up. So, (9) .......... cook for (10) .......... and (11) .......... wash up for (12) .......... .

There's Mrs Peters at number 29 and Mr and Mrs Jarvis next door. Mrs Peters doesn't like painting but she likes making clothes. So (13) .......... is making jumpers for (14) .......... and (15) .......... are painting the kitchen at number 29 for (16) .......... .

My wife and I live with our nine dogs at number 31. Jenny's next door. She's a student. (17) .......... takes the dogs to the park for (18) .......... and (19) .......... buy books for (20) .......... .

But my best neighbour is my twin, Francesca. She's at 35. It was our birthday on Saturday. (21) .......... bought (22) .......... some chocolates and (23) .......... bought (24) .......... some chocolates. Twins are like that!

## FORM AND USE

Look at these sentences
*It's my house.*
*The house belongs to me.*
*The house is mine.*

**POSSESSIVE ADJECTIVES**

**1**   These are the possessive adjectives.
my – **My** *shoes are brown.*
your – **Your** *car is yellow.*
his – **His** *sister is tall.*
her – **Her** *brother is very tall.*
its – *The dog wants its food.*
our – **Our** *holiday was great!*
their – **Their** *house is very cold.*

**2**   We use a possessive adjective before a noun.
*It's my dog.*
*That's her cat.*
*Those are your glasses.*

**POSSESSIVE PRONOUNS**

**1**   These are the possessive pronouns.
mine – *Those jumpers are mine.*
yours – *These shirts are yours.*
his – *The blue bicycle is his.*
hers – *The red bicycle is hers.*

ours – *Those books are ours.*
theirs – *This restaurant is theirs.*
**Note:**
We do not use a possessive pronoun for *it*.

**2**   We never put a noun after a possessive pronoun.
*The dog is mine.*
*The cat is hers.*
*The glasses are yours.*

**3**   A possessive pronoun (*yours, mine*, etc.) replaces a possessive adjective + noun (*your team, my job*).
*My team is better than yours.*
(*My team is better than your team.*)
*Her job is more interesting than mine.*
(*Her job is more interesting than my job.*)
**Note:**
Do not confuse *its* and *it's*: *its* is a possessive adjective;
*it's* = *it is* or *it has*.
*Can you give the dog its food. It's hungry.*

**BELONG TO**
We use *belong to* + an object pronoun.
*The dog belongs to me.*
*The cat belongs to her.*
*The glasses belong to you.*

---

## 1   Complete the sentences

*Complete the sentences with a possessive adjective*
(my, you, his, her, its, our *or* their).
**Examples:**
This bicycle belongs to me. This is *my* bicycle.
These pencils belong to you. These are *your* pencils.

**1**   That book belongs to her. That is ....... book.
**2**   This flat belongs to them. This is ....... flat.
**3**   This parrot belongs to me. This is ....... parrot.
**4**   These socks belong to him. These are ....... socks.
**5**   These shoes belong to me. Those are ....... shoes.
**6**   Those shirts belong to her. Those are ....... shirts.
**7**   That T-shirt belongs to my uncle. That's .......
T-shirt.
**8**   That camera belongs to my wife. That's .......
camera.
**9**   This dog belongs to my children. This is ....... dog.
**10**   That ball belongs to my dog. That's ....... ball.
**11**   This money belongs to you. This is ....... money.
**12**   This car belongs to us. This is ....... car.
**13**   This park belongs to everyone. This is ....... park.
**14**   This motorbike belongs to Mrs Thompson. This is
....... motorbike.

**15**   Those magazines belong to her. Those are .......
magazines.
**16**   These glasses belong to me. They are .......
glasses.
**17**   Those books belong to my husband. They are
....... books.
**18**   This house belongs to my friends. This is .......
house.
**19**   That basket belongs to my cat. That is .......
basket.
**20**   This video belongs to her. This is ....... video.

## 2   Complete the sentences

*Complete the sentences with a possessive adjective.*

**1**   I love fish. Fish is ....... favourite food.
**2**   I have a brother and sister. ....... brother lives in
New Zealand and ....... sister lives in America.
**3**   Jim's a bus driver. He hates ....... job. He wants to
be a film star.
**4**   It's ....... birthday. She's 21 today.
**5**   We didn't send you a postcard. We don't know
....... address.

**6** Do you have sugar in ....... tea?

**7** My grandparents love ....... new house.

**8** Eric is French and ....... wife is Brazilian.

**9** Do you have ....... passport with you?

**10** The twins have ....... birthday party in June.

**11** She washes ....... hair every day.

**12** I have ....... lunch at the office.

**13** We buy ....... food at the supermarket. The food is cheaper there.

**14** They buy ....... food at the market. The people are nicer there.

**15** I buy my fish from a fisherman. ....... fish is always fresh!

**16** Go to my sister's house and see ....... new furniture.

**17** We always have ....... Christmas holidays in Switzerland.

**18** We didn't like ....... old sofa, so we changed ....... cover.

**19** She has ....... breakfast in a café near ....... office.

**20** Have you seen ....... comb? I can't find it.

### 3  Replace the words

*Replace the underlined words with a possessive pronoun (*mine, yours, his, hers, its, ours, yours *or* theirs).
**Example:**
Is that your cake or my cake?
*Is that your cake or mine?*

**1** Is that your newspaper or my newspaper?

**2** Shall we go in my car or your car?

**3** Did you use my computer or her computer?

**4** Is this his sandwich or your sandwich?

**5** Is this our money or their money?

**6** Shall we look at your photographs or our photographs?

**7** Shall we have the party at our house or your house?

**8** Is that our cat or their cat?

**9** Is this your key or my key?

**10** Is this her jumper or his jumper.

**11** Shall we use my flat or your flat?

**12** Is that his dog or her dog?

**13** Did you borrow her coat or his coat?

**14** Is this their umbrella or my umbrella?

**15** Shall we stay at her house or their house?

### 4  Replace the words

*Replace the underlined words with a possessive pronoun.*

**Example:**
My dog is bigger than your dog.
*My dog is bigger than yours.*

**1** His camera is smaller than your camera.

**2** Their garden is bigger than our garden.

**3** Her pronunciation is better than my pronunciation.

**4** My grammar is better than her grammar!

**5** My jokes are better than his jokes!

**6** Our kitchen is smaller than their kitchen.

**7** His bedroom is tidier than her bedroom.

**8** My train is slower than your train. That's why I'm always late.

**9** My parrot is more intelligent than your parrot. My parrot tells jokes.

**10** Your school is bigger than my school.

**11** Her car is faster than his car.

**12** My house is more expensive than their house.

**13** His hair is longer than my hair.

**14** Her mother is older than our mother.

**15** My radio is louder than your radio.

### 5  Choose the correct form

*Choose the correct form in brackets and underline it.*
**Examples:**
I'm going to the cinema with (my / mine) friends tonight.
Shall we listen to your records or (my / mine)?

**1** That's a beautiful piano. Is it (your / yours)?

**2** There's a jumper on the chair. Is it (your / yours) or (my / mine)?

**3** (Her / Hers) bedroom is bigger than (our / ours).

**4** (My / Mine) bag is heavier than (their / theirs).

**5** There's a pen on the table. Is it (our / ours) or (their / theirs).

**6** (My / mine ) watch isn't working today. Is (your / yours)?

**7** (Their / theirs) house is next to (our / ours).

**8** (Our / ours) house is next to (their / theirs).

**9** (Our / ours) winters are colder than (your / yours).

**10** (Our / ours) snowmen are happier than (your / yours)!

**11** (Your / Yours) car is too slow, let's take (my / mine).

**12** Is that (her / hers) hat?

# UNIT 29 Genitive: 's and *whose*
Jenny's pen; Whose pen?

## FORM AND USE

## 1 Complete the story

*Add 's to complete the story. The number in brackets shows how many times to add 's.*
**Example:**
We had lunch at Tony flat. (1)
*We had lunch at* **Tony's** *flat.*

1 We had a party at Jack house yesterday. (1)
2 I went to the party in Gina car and Henry came on Carol motorbike. Fred came on his bicycle. (2)
3 Jack has two children, Jenny and Frank. We put the men coats in Jenny bedroom and the women coats in Frank bedroom. (4)
4 Fred coat is blue and he put his coat in Frank room by mistake. (2)
5 Carol coat is blue. At the end of the party she went to Frank room and took Fred coat by mistake. (3)
6 Fred went to Jenny bedroom and took Carol coat by mistake. (2)
7 Fred went to work today. He was wearing Carol coat. (1)
8 Fred boss is on holiday at the moment. So Fred has

the key to open the office. His secretary was waiting outside in the snow when he arrived. Fred said, 'Good morning,' and put his hand in his pocket for the key. He took out Carol lipstick and gave it to his secretary. 'I can't open the door with this,' the secretary said. Fred face was as red as the lipstick. (3)

## 2 Write the answers

*Write the answers to the questions in the correct form.*
**Examples:**
Where did you buy that bread? (baker)
*at the baker's*
Where did you see Rita? (Mary / house)
*at Mary's house*

1 Where did you buy these oranges? (greengrocer)
2 Where did you buy those biscuits? (grocer)
3 Where did she buy that magazine? (newsagent)
4 Where did you meet George? (John / house)
5 Where did they play football? (David / school)
6 Where did you get that shampoo? (chemist)

7 Where did I leave my keys? (Daisy / house)
8 Where did you see that picture? (Richard / house)
9 Where did you meet your wife? (Peter / guest house)
10 Where did she find that money (Fred / club)
11 Where did you see Alan? (Jane / garden)
12 Where did they buy that watch? (jeweller)

## 3 Put the words in the right order

*Put the words in the right order to make sentences*
**Example:**
What / street / is / the name / this / of?
*What is the name of this street?*

1 I don't / that shirt / the colour / like / of
2 what / Thailand / the capital / of / is?
3 in the middle / the film / of / I fell asleep
4 what / the meaning / that word / of / is?
5 I'll meet / at the front / the station / you / of
6 what / that mountain / the name / is / of?
7 what / the telephone number / of / is / the restaurant?
8 what / the address / of / is / The White House?
9 I / of / met / Jenny / 1997 / the spring / in
10 this is / a photograph / my school / of
11 this food / the / I / of / taste / like
12 at the back/ the house/ is / of / the garden

## 4 Write questions

*Write questions with* Whose + *verb* to be, *and complete the answers.*
**Examples:**
Whose / pencil / this?
*Whose pencil is this ?*
*It's* Tim's.
Whose / pencils / those?
*Whose pencils are those?*
*They're* Tim's.

1 Whose / book / this?
.......... Tina's.
2 Whose / books / these?
.......... Tina's.
3 Whose / dog / that?
.......... my sister's.
4 Whose / biscuits / these?
.......... Robert's.
5 Whose / parrot / that?
.......... my uncle's.

6 Whose / radio / this?
.......... Joan's.
7 Whose / newspapers / these?
.......... Aunt Beryl's.
8 Whose / computer / that?
.......... my brother's.
9 Whose / CDs / these?
.......... Harriet's.
10 Whose / answers / these?
.......... mine!
11 Whose / keys / those?
.......... John's
12 Whose / television / this?
.......... my father's.

## 5 Write questions and answers

**Examples:**
Whose / this?
*Whose is this?*
*It's mine.* (it belongs to me)
Whose / those?
*Whose are those?*
*They're his.* (they belong to him)

1 Whose / that?
.......... (it belongs to them)
2 Whose / these?
.......... (they belong to me)
3 Whose / this?
.......... (it belongs to me)
4 Whose / that?
.......... (it belongs to her)
5 Whose / these?
.......... (they belong to us)
6 Whose / those?
.......... (they belong to her)
7 Whose / that?
.......... (it belongs to us)
8 Whose / these?
.......... (they belong to you)
9 Whose those?
.......... (they belong to him)
10 Whose / this?
.......... (it belongs to you)
11 Whose / those?
.......... (they belong to him)
12 Whose / that
..........(it belongs to me)

## COUNTABLE NOUNS

**1**    Most nouns have a singular form and a plural form.

*I ate **a banana**.    I ate **ten bananas**.*

*Banana* is a countable noun. We can count bananas. Nouns like *car, train, book, table, elephant, parrot, shirt* are countable.

**2**    We use *a, an* and *the* with the singular form of countable nouns.

We use *the*, no article (see Unit 25), *some, a lot of* and *many* with the plural form of countable nouns.

***the** cars, **trains**, **some** books, **a lot of** elephants, **many** parrots*

**3**    We use *many* and *how many* with the plural form of countable nouns.

*There aren't **many** tourists here in the winter.*

***How many** sisters do you have?*

We usually use *many* for negative sentences and *a lot of* for positive sentences.

*There **aren't many** biscuits.*

*She's got **a lot of** friends.*

## UNCOUNTABLE NOUNS

**1**    Some nouns have only one form. They are always singular.

*The weather **is** good.* (never *The weathers are good*.) We call these uncountable nouns. We cannot count them.

**2**    We can use *the*, no article, *some, a lot of* and *much* with uncountable nouns. We cannot use *a, an* or *many* with uncountable nouns.

***the** cheese, **bread**, **some** toast, **a lot of** luggage, **much** information*

Nouns like *cheese, bread, toast, luggage, news, information, music* and *homework* are uncountable.

**3**    We cannot say *two waters* or *three breads*, but we can use words like *pieces, slices, cups, glasses, items* with uncountable nouns to make them countable.

*two **bottles** of water*

*three **slices** of bread*

*some **pieces** of paper*

**4**    Nouns like *gold, petrol* and *rice* are uncountable. But we can use measurements like *kilos, litres, pints, grams* to make them countable.

*two **kilos** of gold*

*twenty **litres** of petrol*

*500 **grams** of rice*

**5**    Some important nouns (like *coffee* and *sugar*) are different. We can use them countably or uncountably but the meaning changes.

**As an uncountable noun**

*Britain buys a lot of **coffee** from Brazil.*

*There is a lot of **sugar** in chocolate.*

**As a countable noun**

*Shall I make you **a coffee**?* (= a cup of coffee)

*I have **five sugars** in my tea.* (= five spoonfuls of sugar)

The uncountable meaning is more general.

**6**    We use *much* and *how much* with uncountable nouns.

*We haven't got **much** milk.*

***How much** homework do you have tonight?*

We usually use *much* for negative sentences and *a lot of* for positive sentences.

*I haven't got **much** money.*

*This car uses **a lot of** petrol.*

---

### 1    Tick the uncountable nouns

*Tick the uncountable nouns in the list. The first one has been done for you.*

1 petrol ☑ 2 parrot ☐ 3 friend ☐ 4 cup ☐
5 elephant ☐ 6 knife ☐ 7 joke ☐ 8 electricity ☐
9 money ☐ 10 night ☐ 11 office ☐ 12 knife ☐
13 biscuit ☐ 14 luggage ☐ 15 car ☐ 16 tourist ☐
17 year ☐ 18 basket ☐ 19 example ☐ 20 news ☐
21 furniture ☐ 22 fork ☐ 23 information ☐
24 table ☐ 25 rice ☐ 26 gold ☐

### 2    Make the nouns countable

*Match the uncountable nouns with a word or words in the box to make them countable. Some words will be used more than once. The first one has been done for you.*

| bars | cups | glasses | items |
|------|------|---------|-------|
| pieces | litres | slices | spoonfuls |

1    gold        *bars / pieces of gold*
2    milk    .............................
3    water    .............................
4    coffee    .............................
5    bread    .............................

6 sugar ............................
7 paper ............................
8 chocolate ............................
9 news ............................
10 fruit ............................
11 information ............................

## 3 Complete the sentences

*Complete the sentences with* much *or* many.

**Example:**

Is the cinema expensive? How *much* money do we need?

1 Do you know .......... Spanish songs?
2 Do you listen to .......... music?
3 How .......... sugars do you have in your tea?
4 We don't have .......... sugar. Can you buy some today?
5 It's a very small hotel. It doesn't have .......... rooms.
6 Did she have .......... luggage?
7 We don't have .......... petrol in the car. Is there a petrol station near here?
8 Do you have .......... homework to do tonight?
9 There are .......... hot days in the desert and we don't have .......... rain.
10 Were there .......... people on the train?
11 Do you drink .......... coffee?
12 Have you drunk .......... cups of coffee today?
13 How .......... friends came to your party?
14 Did you have .......... work to do today?
15 We don't get .......... snow here.
16 There aren't .......... cinemas in this town.
17 But there are .......... cafes.
18 You don't see .......... dogs on the beach.
19 There's been an accident, but we don't have .......... information.
20 Do you like .......... sugar in your coffee?

## 4 Complete the questions

*You are going to make a cake with your nephew, Harry. Harry is asking you some questions. Complete the questions with* How much *or* How many.

**Examples:**

*How much* water do we need?
*How many* plates do we need?

1 ...... dishes do we need?
2 ...... spoons do we need?
3 ..... eggs do we need?
4 ..... flour do we need?
5 ..... sugar do we need?
6 ..... milk do we need?
7 ..... grams of butter do we need?
8 ..... chocolate can we add?
9 ..... bananas do we need?
10 ..... cream do we need?
11 ..... nuts can we put in?
12 ..... minutes will you cook it for?
13 ..... people will eat this cake?
14 ..... slices can I have?
15 ..... more cakes will you make?

## 5 Write the correct form

Complete the sentences below by writing the correct form of the noun in brackets. If it is countable add 's'; if it is uncountable, do not add 's'.

1 There were a lot of traffic (accident) in the bad weather.
2 They have some good (film) at that cinema.
3 The teacher always gives them a lot of (home work).
4 Can you give me any (information) about the hotel?
5 They've just bought some new (furniture).
6 A lot of (tourist) go to Bali.
7 They like the beautiful (scenery).
8 I spent a lot of (money) in that shop. I haven't got any left now. I'll have to walk home.
9 They've bought some new (equipment) for the factory. It's very modern now.
10 I want some (tea).
11 And get me two jars of (coffee).
12 They play a lot of different (music) every day.
13 The painter did a lot of (work) in the house; but the owner refused to pay him.
14 If there isn't any (bread), give them some cake.
15 She enjoys all (sport), especially tennis.
16 There isn't a lot of (time) before the train goes.
17 We need some (example) for this exercise.
18 I don't like the (water) here. It's very dirty.
19 He collected foreign (coin).
20 Mary doesn't eat (meat) now.

# UNIT 31 *some / any*
## I need some shirts; I haven't got any shirts

## USE

Look at these sentences.
*I have bought **some** fruit.*
*He has got **some** language course books.*
*They didn't sell **any** cars last week.*
*She won't buy **any** bread from that shop.*
*Have you got **any** coffee?*
*Will you be with **any** friends on holiday?*

**SOME**
**1**   We use *some* to show a quantity when we do not know how much or how many.
*She went to the shop to get some eggs.*
**2**   We use *some* in positive statements with both countable and uncountable nouns.
*Mrs Gill bought **some eggs** at the grocer's and **some meat** at the butcher's.*

**ANY**
We use *any* in negative statements or questions.
*I didn't see any birds in the park.*
*Did you take any photographs of your holiday?*
**Notes:**
**1**   We can use *some* in questions when we think the answer will be 'Yes'.
*Have you got some money for the tickets.*
**2** We can use some for offers
*Would you like some tea?*
or requests
*Can I have some coffee, please?*

### 1   Complete the sentences

*Complete the sentences with* a, an *or* some.
**Examples:**
I had *a* banana and *an* orange for lunch.
We're on holiday next week. I hope we have *some* good weather.

1   He bought .......... gold and put it in the bank.
2   Shall we listen to .......... music?
3   I'm hungry. I'm going to make .......... sandwich. I'll need .......... bread, .......... butter, .......... cheese and .......... onions. Then I'll need .......... plate and .......... knife. You need a lot of things to make .......... sandwich. Perhaps I'm not really hungry and there's .......... chocolate in the fridge.
4   There are .......... beautiful mountains near here.
5   I have .......... Italian penfriend. I sent her .......... pictures of my dog. She sent me .......... book. The book has .......... information about .......... famous museums in Rome and .......... wonderful beach in Sicily. I think my dog needs .......... holiday.

### 2   Make the sentences questions

**Example:**
You've got some flowers.
*Have you got any flowers?*

1   There is some money on the table.
2   He bought some books yesterday.
3   She has already sold some old furniture.
4   They will fetch some water.
5   He must bring some food with him.
6   They've got some work today.
7   There was some rain yesterday.
8   There are some cars parked near the school.
9   They've got some visitors.
10   He saw some films on television.

### 3   Make the sentences negative

*Make the sentences negative. Use* not ... any.
**Example:**
I have some luggage.
*I don't have any luggage.*

1   We have some trees in our garden.
2   We have some butter in the fridge.
3   We have some big mountains near here.
4   They have some questions.
5   She has some news.
6   He has some flour in the kitchen cupboard.
7   This town has some good cinemas.
8   We had some snow in the winter.
9   We had some tea on the plane yesterday.
10   We had some homework to do yesterday.

# UNIT 24-31 Unit Revision Test 3

*The questions in Revision Test 3 are about the grammar in Units 24–32. Choose the best answer, A, B or C.*

## UNITS 24-25

1 I have .... Irish penfriend.
   A a          B an          C nice
2 Madrid is .... European city.
   A a          B an          C m
3 We played tennis for .... hour and a half.
   A a          B an          C —
4 She's .... .
   A a teacher  B an teacher  C teacher
5 I work for eight hours .... day.
   A the        B a           C an
6 We live near .... Himalayas.
   A the        B an          C a
7 Don't look at .... sun. It's bad for your eyes.
   A a          B —           C the
8 Do you .... ?
   A violin play  B the violin  C play
                    play         the violin

## UNITS 26-27

9 .... soup is delicious!
   A This       B These       C Those
10 Hi, Sarah. .... is Jenny. Can I speak to Sam?
   A That       B Speaking    C This
11 .... Sarah? Hi, this is Jenny. Can I speak to Sam?
   A Is that    B This is     C Those are
12 She phoned .... yesterday.
   A I          B me          C we
13 We saw .... in the park.
   A them       B they        C he
14 .... has got a new car.
   A Them       B They        C He
15 Jenny has three dogs. She takes .... to the park.
   A them       B we          C they
16 Can you help .... ? This bag is very heavy.
   A I          B me          C we

## UNITS 28-29

17 This is .... dog.
   A me         B mine        C my
18 Those are .... glasses.
   A her        B hers        C theirs
19 This bicycle belongs to .... .
   A I          B my          C me
20 Those books belong to .... .
   A him        B his         C he

21 Can you give the dog .... food?
   A it's       B its         C it
22 .... very cold today!
   A It's       B Its         C It
23 There's a blue jumper on the chair. Is it .... ?
   A me or you  B my or your  C mine or
                                 yours
24 Is that .... bicycle?
   A Jim        B of Jim      C Jim's
25 I bought these oranges at .... .
   A the        B the         C the
     greengrocer   greengrocers'   greengrocer's
26 She sat at the .... .
   A train's front  B front train  C front of the
                                     train
27 Whose .... ?
   A that pen is  B pen is that  C of pen is
                                   that
28 Whose .... ?
   A are these   B these        C belong
     books         books are      these books

## UNITS 30-31

29 The .... good.
   A weather is  B weathers is  C weathers
                                  are
30 Britain buys ... coffee from Brazil.
   A many        B an           C a lot of
31 There aren't .... tourists here in the winter.
   A much        B many         C a
32 .... brothers do you have?
   A How much    B Much         C How many
33 We haven't got .... milk.
   A much        B many         C a lot of
34 .... homework do we have tonight?
   A How much    B How many     C A lot of
35 They don't have .... friends.
   A a           B some         C any
36 Can I have .... tea, please?
   A many        B some         C any
37 She bought some cheese and three .... of bread.
   A loaf        B loafs        C loaves
38 They have five .... .
   A child       B children     C childrens
39 The farmer has 112 cows and 154 .... .
   A ships       B sheep        C sheeps
40 All big .... are the same. They're noisy and dirty.
   A city        B citys        C cities

## FORM AND USE

**ADJECTIVES**

**1** Look at these sentences.

*She drives a **French** car.*

*This bread is **wonderful**!*

*Can you give me that **blue** jumper?*

The words in bold are adjectives.

**2** Adjectives give information about people and things.

*a **tall** woman, a **beautiful** park, a **sunny** day*

*Can you make me some dinner? I'm **tired** and **hungry**.*

**3** We usually put adjectives before a noun.

*a **green** car, an **old** building, a **beautiful** photograph*

**4** We put adjectives after the verb *to be*.

*the car **is green**, the building **is old**, that photograph **is beautiful***

**5** We often use adjectives after verbs like *look, sound, feel, taste* and *smell*.

*You **look happy**!*

*Those flowers **smell wonderful**.*

*This soup **tastes good**.*

**6** Adjectives have only one form. There is no plural.

*an **expensive** car – three **expensive cars*** (not *three expensives cars*)

**7** When we have two or more adjectives before a noun, we put these adjectives in a special order. Look at this example:

*a **blue**, **plastic** cup*

We say the colour (*blue*) before the material (*plastic*). The usual order is:

| | | | | |
|---|---|---|---|---|
| **1** | **opinion** + | nice | beautiful | wonderful |
| **2** | **size** + | tall | short | large |
| **3** | **age** + | new | old | young |
| **4** | **colour** + | red | blue | yellow |
| **5** | **nationality** + | French | Spanish | Italian |
| **6** | **material** + | wooden | plastic | cotton |
| | **noun** | | | |

*He has a **small, brown** dog.* (2 + 4)

*She lives in a **beautiful, old** house.* (1 + 3)

*They drive a **big, old, Italian** car.* (2 + 3 + 5)

### 1    Make sentences

*Put the words in the right order to make sentences.*

**Example:**

man / a / he / is / rich

*He is a rich man.*

1   this / good / smells / soup
2   love / trousers / yellow / I / those
3   dangerous / looks / dog / white / that
4   hot / feel / I
5   they / happy / sound
6   tired / look / you
7   sad / very / look / those tourists
8   tastes / wonderful / bread / this
9   they / hungry in the afternoon / always / feel
10   milk / fresh / bought / I've / some

### 2    Complete the sentences

*Choose an adjective and a noun to complete the sentences. Use each word once. The first one has been done for you.*

| **Adjectives** | **Nouns** |
|---|---|
| foreign | sport √ |
| favourite √ | winters |
| cold | book |
| expensive | people |
| friendly | fruit |
| interesting | biscuits |
| beautiful | beaches |
| fresh | languages |
| strong | journey |
| dangerous | tea |
| chocolate | restaurant |

1   My *favourite sport* is tennis.
2   We have very ........ ........ here. It snows every day.
3   It's an .......... .......... . We paid £23 for pizza!
4   I'm reading an .......... .......... at the moment. It's about Brazilian parrots.
5   I bought some .......... .......... at the market today.
6   Thailand is wonderful. It has .......... .......... with soft white sand.
7   Paris is full of .......... .......... . Everyone smiles and says 'hello'.
8   They drove 3,000 km across the desert. It was a .......... .......... .
9   I'm tired and thirsty. I need some .......... .......... .
10   She speaks three .......... .......... .
11   I was very hungry this afternoon. I ate a packet of .......... .......... .

## 3 Complete the story

*Complete the story. Put the adjectives in brackets in the right order. The first one has been done for you.*

One day, Fred was getting dressed in his (**1**) *big, old* (old / big) house in Birmingham when he looked at his (**2**) .......... (plastic / brown / old) shoes and thought, 'I need some new shoes!'

So he got into his (**3**) .......... (new / beautiful / Korean / red) car and drove to the (**4**) .......... (new / nice) airport near Birmingham and took a plane to the (**5**) .......... (old / Italian / wonderful) city of Milan, famous for its shoes.

Fred took a (**6**) .......... (yellow / nice / new) taxi from the airport to a street with a hundred shoe shops.

Fred walked into the first shop and sat down on a (**7**) .......... (wooden / blue / small) chair. A (**8**) .......... (tall / Italian / beautiful) lady came to him and said, 'Can I help you, sir?'

'I want some (**9**) .......... (new/ nice) shoes,' Fred said.

'Well, this is the street of a hundred shoe shops,' she said. 'And we can start with these (**10**) .......... (leather / French / brown / nice) shoes here.'

Fred tried the shoes but he didn't like them. So, the (**11**) .......... (tall / Italian / beautiful) lady took the (**12**) .......... (leather / French / brown / nice) shoes away and came back with some different shoes.

'These are good,' she said. 'These are (**13**) .......... (lovely / Spanish / new / leather) shoes. They arrived today.'

Fred tried the shoes but he didn't like them. So, the (**14**) .......... (tall / Italian / beautiful) lady took the (**15**) .......... (lovely / Spanish / new / leather) shoes away and came back with some different shoes.

Fred didn't like the (**16**) .......... (wooden / Dutch / nice) shoes or the (**17**) .......... (blue / plastic / American) shoes or the (**18**) .......... (cotton / yellow) shoes from India.

'This is the street of a hundred shoe shops,' the (**19**) .......... (tall / Italian / beautiful) lady said. 'But we don't have any shoes you like, sir.'

Then suddenly Fred saw some shoes he liked. 'Those (**20**) .......... (plastic / brown) shoes are nice,' said Fred. 'Yes, I've decided. I'll buy them.'

'I'm sorry sir,' the lady said. 'You can't buy those (**21**) .......... (plastic / brown) shoes. They are yours! You were wearing them when you came in!'

---

### AS ... AS

We use *as* + adjective + *as* when two things or two people are the same.
*Terry is 1.59m tall. Jutta is 1.59m tall. Jutta is* **as tall as** *Terry.*

We use *not* + *as* + adjective + *as* when two things or two people are different.
*Terry weighs 71 kg. Jutta weighs 73 kg. Terry is* **not as heavy as** *Jutta.*

## 4 Make comparisons

*Make positive and negative comparisons. Use* as ... as *or* not as ... as.

**Examples:**
Tim has £1 in the bank. Ben has £1 in the bank.
Tim / be / rich / Ben
*Tim is as rich as Ben.*
I am 23 years old. Gina is 24 years old.
I / be / not / old / Gina
*I am not as old as Gina.*

1 Kelly is twelve years old. Veronica is twelve years old.
Kelly / be / old / Veronica
2 Veronica is twelve years old. Debbie is fifteen years old.
Veronica / be / not / old / Debbie
3 Debbie is 1.53 m tall. James is 1.53 m tall.
Debbie / be / tall / James
4 James can run 100 metres in fifteen seconds. Tim can run 100 metres in fifteen seconds.
James / be / fast / Tim
5 Tim has £3 in the bank. Tessa has £3,000,000 in the bank.
Tim / be / not / rich / Tessa
6 Tessa is twenty-seven years old. Kelly is twelve years old.
Tessa / be / not / young / Kelly

# UNIT 33   Adjectives 2: Comparative Form
## bigger; more famous

## FORM

**1** Look at these sentences.
*An orange is **sweeter than** a potato.*
*A train is **faster than** a bus.*
*Gold is **more expensive** than sugar.*
These are comparative sentences.

**2** For adjectives of one syllable, add *-er*.
*quick – quicker, slow – slower, tall – taller, cheap – cheaper*
*The train is **quicker than** the bus.*

**3** For most adjectives with two syllables, and all adjectives with three syllables or more, put *more* in front of the adjective.
*famous – more famous, beautiful – more beautiful, interesting – more interesting*
*This exercise is **more difficult than** the first one.*

**4** For short adjectives that end in *-y*, change the *-y* to *-i* then add *-er*.
*happy – happier, easy – easier*

**5** For short adjectives that end in *-e*, just add *-r*.
*nice – nicer*

**6** Be careful with short adjectives that end in vowel + consonant.
When you hear the consonant, double the last letter and then add *-er*.
*hot – hotter, big – bigger, thin – thinner*
When you do not hear the consonant, just add *-er*.
*new – newer*

**7** There are some irregular adjectives. Here are the two most important.
*good – better*
*Your ice-cream is **better than** mine.*
*bad – worse*
*The weather is **worse** today **than** yesterday.*

**8** We normally use *than* after a comparative
*She's **richer than** me. I'm **poorer than** her.*
but we sometimes drop *than* when the meaning is clear.
*New York is expensive. But Tokyo is **more expensive**.*
*(= Tokyo is **more expensive than** New York.)*
*The Atlantic is big. But the Pacific is **bigger**.*
*(= The Pacific is **bigger than** the Atlantic.)*

**9** There is also a negative form that we saw in Unit 32.
I'm / You're / We're / They're
*not + as + adjective + as*
He's / She's / It's
*not + as + adjective + as*
*Greenland **isn't as hot as** Africa. (= Africa is hotter than Greenland.)*
*Rome **isn't as beautiful as** Paris. (= Paris is more beautiful than Rome.)*
*Jane **isn't as tall as** Fred. (= Fred is taller than Jane.)*

## USE

We use a comparative adjective to compare two things or two people.
*Jane is 21 years old. Carol is 23 years old.*
*Jane is **younger than** Carol.*
or
*Carol is **older than** Jane.*

*You can buy a bicycle for £100. You can buy a car for £10,000.*
*A bicycle is **cheaper than** a car.*
or
*A car is **more expensive than** a bicycle.*

### 1   Write the comparative

*Write the comparative form of these adjectives. The first one has been done for you.*

| | | |
|---|---|---|
| 1 | small | *smaller* |
| 2 | dark | ................... |
| 3 | big | ................... |
| 4 | tall | ................... |
| 5 | easy | ................... |
| 6 | hard | ................... |
| 7 | cold | ................... |
| 8 | hot | ................... |
| 9 | important | ................... |
| 10 | heavy | ................... |
| 11 | interesting | ................... |
| 12 | happy | ................... |
| 13 | nice | ................... |
| 14 | good | ................... |
| 15 | beautiful | ................... |

## 2 Make comparisons

**Examples:**

My uncle / old / my brother
*My uncle is older than my brother.*
An elephant / big / a cat
*An elephant is bigger than a cat.*

1  Fred / tall / Jane
2  A train / fast / a car
3  A plane / fast / train
4  A bicycle / cheap / a motorbike
5  A motorbike / expensive / a bicycle
6  Africa / hot / Greenland
7  A mountain / big / hill
8  An ocean / big / a sea
9  My boss / rich / me
10 I / happy / my boss
11 Tennis / interesting / football
12 Her bedroom / big / her kitchen
13 A computer / expensive / a typewriter
14 Tea / nice / coffee
15 English / difficult / my language

## 3 Complete the sentences

*Complete the sentences with the comparative form of the adjective in brackets.*

**Examples:**

Can you carry my bag for me? You're *stronger* than I am. (strong)

I've got a new job. It's *more interesting* than my old one. (interesting)

1  I love the countryside. It's .......... than the city. (clean)
2  Look at my new camera. It's .......... than my hand. (small)
3  Let's go to the beach. It's .......... than the office on a hot day. (nice)
4  I like these old shoes. They're .......... than my new ones. (comfortable)
5  Let's eat fruit today. It's .......... than fast food. (good)
6  Let's eat fast food today. It's .......... than fruit. (cheap)
7  Can you waterski? It's .......... than skiing. (difficult)
8  Take the train. It's .......... than the bus. (quick)
9  We've bought a new house. It's .......... than the old one. (big)
10 My sister has a swimming pool in her house. She's .......... than me! (rich)

## 4 Complete the sentences

*Complete the sentences with the comparative form of an adjective. The first one has been done for you.*

1  The white bread is fresh but the brown bread is *fresher*.
2  The train is fast but the plane is .......... .
3  Spain is hot but Kenya is .......... .
4  Canada is cold but Greenland is .......... .
5  Your first idea was interesting but your second idea was .......... .
6  Rome is beautiful but Paris is .......... .
7  The weather was bad yesterday but today it's .........!
8  George is tall but his sister is .......... .
9  Be careful! The brown dog is dangerous but the white dog is .......... .
10 This exercise was easy. Is the next one .......... ?

## 5 Make comparisons

*Make comparisons. Use the negative comparative form of the adjective.*

**Examples:**

A plane is faster than a train.
A train *is not as fast as a plane*. (fast)
My sister is richer than me.
I'm *not as rich as my sister*. (rich)

1  An elephant is stronger than a cat.
   A cat .......... (strong)
2  Indonesia is bigger than Sri Lanka.
   Sri Lanka .......... (big)
3  Helen is taller than Jim.
   Jim .......... (tall)
4  An apple is sweeter than a tomato.
   A tomato .......... (sweet)
5  A computer is more expensive than a typewriter.
   A typewriter .......... (expensive)
6  You're stronger than me.
   I'm .......... (strong)
7  A car is quicker than a bicycle.
   A bicycle .......... (quick)
8  A mile is bigger than a kilometre.
   A kilometre .......... (big)

# Adjectives 3: Superlative Form
## the biggest; the most famous

## FORM

**1**   Look at these sentences.
*My uncle is* **the richest** *man in America!*
*This is* **the fastest** *train in the world.*
*That's* **the best** *film I've ever seen.*
These are superlative sentences.
**2**   For adjectives of one syllable, use *the* + adjective + *-est*.
*small – the smallest, tall – the tallest, big – the biggest*
*He is* **the oldest** *person in the world.*
**3**   For adjectives with two syllables, we normally use *the most* + adjective.
*careful – the most careful, famous – the most famous*
*Clare is the* **most careless** *writer in the class.*
But there are many exceptions
*funny – the funniest, happy – the happiest, easy – the easiest, dirty – the dirtiest, noisy – the noisiest*
**4**   For adjectives with three or more syllables we always use *the most* + adjective
*dangerous – the most dangerous, important – the most important, expensive – the most expensive*
*Tom bought* **the most expensive** *shoes in the shop.*

**But:**
**5**   For short adjectives that end in *-e* add *-st*.
*large – the largest*
**6**   For adjectives ending in *-y,* the *-y* changes to *-iest*.
*heavy – the heaviest, easy – the easiest*
**7**   For short adjectives that end with a vowel + consonant, double the last letter when you hear the consonant.
*thin – the thinnest*
When you do not hear the consonant, add *-est*
*new – the newest*
**8**   There are some irregular superlatives. The two most important are
*good – the best*
*This is the* **best pizza** *I've ever eaten.*
*bad – the worst*
*That's the* **worst joke** *I've ever heard!*
**9**   We often use a superlative without a noun.
*We visited Rome, Venice and Milan. They are all beautiful but I think Rome is the most beautiful.*

## USE

We use a superlative when we compare more than two things or people.
*Jane is 21 years old. Carol is 23 years old. Fiona is 33 years old.*
*Jane is* **the youngest** *and Fiona is* **the oldest**.
*You can buy a bicycle for £100, a motorbike for £500*
*and a car for £10,000.*
*The bicycle is* **the cheapest** *and the car is* **the most expensive**.

### 1   Write the superlative

*Write the superlative form of these adjectives.*
**Examples:**
rich *the richest*
interesting *the most interesting*

1   happy ...................
2   important ...................
3   beautiful ...................
4   big ...................
5   new ...................
6   strong ...................
7   hard ...................
8   nice ...................
9   large ...................
10   noisy ...................
11   good ...................
12   easy ...................
13   bad ...................
14   difficult ...................
15   young ...................

### 2   Complete the sentences

*Complete the sentences with the superlative form of the adjective in brackets.*
**Example:**
Rice is *the most popular* (popular) food in the world.

1   Tea is ................... (popular) drink in China.
2   Tokyo is ................... (big) city in Japan.
3   Basketball is ................... (popular) sport in America.
4   Skiing is ................... (enjoyable) sport I know.
5   Manchester is ................... (wet) city in England.

6 The Kalahari desert is ................... (dry) place on earth.
7 February is ................... (short) month of the year.
8 In Britain, 21st June is ................... (long) day of the year.
9 The lion is ................... (strong) animal of all.
10 The sun is ................... (hot) thing in the sky.

## 3 Make sentences

*Put the adjectives in brackets into the correct form. Then put the words in the right order to make sentences.*
**Example:**
tea / in the world / (popular) / is / drink
*Tea is the most popular drink in the world.*

1 Guyana / (small) country / is / in South America
2 Greenland / (big) / in the world / the country / is
3 in / Brazil / the Amazon / (long) river / is
4 in Africa / the Sahara / (big) desert / is
5 (big) / the Atlantic / is / ocean / in the world
6 (high) mountain / Kilimanjaro / is / in Africa
7 in Japan / (beautiful) / Kyoto / is / city
8 in the world / New York / (exciting) city / is
9 The Eiffel Tower / (famous) / in France / is / building
10 Australia / (big) island / the world / is / in

## 4 Make sentences

*Make sentences with the correct superlative form of the adjective and the past participle of the verb in brackets.*
**Examples:**
This is *the best* (good) ice-cream I've ever *eaten* (eat).
She's the *most interesting* (interesting) person I've ever *met* (meet).

1 This is ............... (enjoyable) holiday we've ever ............... (have).
2 That is ............... (funny) joke I've ever ............... (hear)!
3 This is ............... (good) spaghetti you've ever ............... (cook).
4 That's ............... (big) fish he's ever ............... (catch).
5 Paris is ............... (beautiful) city she's ever ............... (visit).
6 'Love Story' is ............... (good) film I've ever ............... (see).
7 'Life and Love' is ............... (interesting) book they've ever ............... (read).

8 This is ............... (dangerous) thing I've ever ............... (do).
9 That's ............... (bad) photograph you've ever ............... (take).
10 My blue bicycle is ............... (useful) thing I've ever ............... (buy).

## 5 Complete the dialogues

*Complete the dialogues with the superlative form of the adjective. The first one has been done for you.*

1 **Tony:** How was your holiday?
  **Karen:** We had a great time. We went to Chicago, Los Angeles and Washington. Chicago was *the most interesting* (interesting), Los Angeles was ............... (exciting) and Washington was ............... (clean) and ............... (beautiful)!

2 **Brigitte:** What's the ............... (good) way to get from Rome to Beijing.
  **Travel Agent:** Well, ............... (quick) way is to fly, ............... (enjoyable) way is to go by train, and ............... (cheap) way is to walk!

3 **John:** Did you enjoy the film?
  **Patricia:** Yes and no. We were in the ............... (expensive) seats in the cinema, but I was sitting behind the ............... (tall) man I've ever seen. On my left, there was a woman with the ............... (loud) voice I've ever heard. She talked all the time. And on my right, there was a man with the ............... (dirty) dog I've ever seen. Behind me there was a small boy who ate the ............... (noisy) popcorn in the world, and on the ............... (cold) day of the year all the doors in the cinema were open. I think the film was good, but I'm not really sure.

# UNIT 35 Adverbs
## slowly, beautifully

## FORM

**1** Look at these sentences.
*He writes **beautifully**.*
*They ran **quickly**.*
*Do they sing **well**?*
The <u>underlined</u> words are adverbs.

**2** To make an adverb, we normally add *-ly* to an adjective.

| Adjective | Adverb |
|---|---|
| *slow* | *slowly* |
| *quick* | *quickly* |
| *beautiful* | *beautifully* |
| *quiet* | *quietly* |

**3** For short adjectives ending in *-y*, change to *-ily*.
*happy – happily, heavy – heavily, easy – easily*

**4** There are some irregular adverbs.
*He works **hard**. (not He works hardly.)*
*She drives **fast**. (not She drives fastly.)*
**Note:**
With *hard* and *fast*, the adverb is the same as the adjective.

**5** Be careful with *well*, which has two different meanings.
**A** the adverb form of *good*
*She is a **good** swimmer. She swims **well**.*
**B** an adjective we use to talk about our health.
*Are you **well**? Yes, thanks, I'm very **well**.*

**6** An adverb follows a verb.

| | |
|---|---|
| *He's a **bad** dancer.* | (adjective + noun) |
| *He dances **badly**.* | (verb + adverb) |
| *We had a **quick** lunch.* | (adjective + noun) |
| *We ate **quickly**.* | (verb + adverb) |

**7** We normally use adverbs in two forms.
**A** verb + adverb
*She **eats quickly**.*
*Please **speak slowly**.*
**B** verb + object + adverb
*He sings **those songs beautifully**.*
*She read **the map carefully**.*
Notice how we often put the adverb at the end of the sentence. Compare this with how we use adverbs of frequency (Unit 36).

## USE

Adjectives and adverbs look similar. But they do different things.
**1** Generally, an adjective answers the question *What?*
***What** colour is the shirt? The shirt is **blue**.*
It tells you about a noun *(the shirt)*.
**2** An adverb answers the question How?
***How** does she sing? She sings **beautifully**.*
It tells you about a verb *(sings)*.

### 1 Complete the sentences

*Complete these sentences with an adverb.*
**Example:**
He is a <u>slow</u> worker. He works *slowly*.

1 He's a *bad* driver. He drives ..................... .
2 She's a *careful* driver. She drives ..................... .
3 She's a *hard* worker. She works ..................... .
4 He's a *beautiful* singer. He sings ..................... .
5 She's a *fast* runner. She runs ..................... .
6 He's a *good* player. He plays ..................... .
7 He thinks English is *easy*. He learns ..................... .
8 The rain is *heavy*. It's raining ..................... .
9 The train is *slow*. We're going ..................... .
10 The children are *happy*. They are playing ..................... .
11 He's a *quiet* worker. He works ..................... .
12 She's a *bad* dancer. She dances ..................... .
13 He's a *quick* learner. He learns ..................... .
14 This car is *fast*. It's going ..................... .
15 She's a *good* painter. She paints ..................... .

### 2 Choose the correct adverb

Choose the correct adverb in brackets and <u>underline</u> it.
**Example:**
Please speak (quickly / *slowly*). I can't understand English very well.

1 Please drive (carefully / dangerously). The roads are very wet.
2 Please talk (quietly / loudly). I'm trying to work.
3 Let's run (fast / slowly). The bus is coming!
4 He looks sad. I think he did (well / badly) in the exam.
5 You sound happy. Did you do (well / badly) in the exam?

**6** I saw Tim at the dentist's. He was sitting there (nervously / happily).

**7** She's the best dancer at our school. She dances really (beautifully / badly).

**8** He's the worst singer at our school. He sings really (beautifully / badly).

**9** I have some new glasses. Now I can see things (clearly / badly).

**10** We were in a restaurant. He was eating (noisily / quietly) and everyone was looking at him. 'Please eat (nicely / badly),' I said, but he just laughed at me. So I stood up and left the restaurant (happily / angrily).

**11** We're late. We must eat dinner (slowly / quickly).

**12** Before her French exam she studied her dictionary (carefully / dangerously).

**13** He's the best worker in the office. He works (hard / badly).

**14** I saw Jane at the station. Her boyfriend was late and she was waiting (angrily / happily).

**15** He's the best driver I know. He drives (well / badly).

## 3 Complete the sentences

*Complete the sentences with* well *or* good.
**Example:**
This food is *good*. You cook *well*!

**1** Can you swim ...............?

**2** He bought a ............... camera. It was very expensive.

**3** She plays the piano four hours a day. She plays ............... .

**4** We had fish for lunch. The fish wasn't fresh. I don't feel .............. .

**5** She's a ............... teacher. She teaches ............... .

**6** Good morning. Did you sleep...............?

**7** That's a ............... question! I don't know the answer.

**8** Their grammar is ............... . They speak English ............... .

**9** How's your brother? Is he ...............?

**10** Do you know her ...............?

**11** How was your dinner? Did you eat .....?

**12** She makes very ............... coffee.

**13** They trained hard for the football match and played ............... .

**14** My mother lived in Spain for ten years, and speaks the language ............... .

**15** He's a ............... painter.

## 4 Choose the correct form

*Choose the correct form, adjective or adverb, and* underline *it.*
**Example:**
This bag is very (heavy / heavily). What's in it?

**1** It was snowing (heavy / heavily) when the plane arrived.

**2** We lost the game. I played well but the others played (bad / badly).

**3** That dog is (dangerous / dangerously). Be careful!

**4** I'm very thirsty. I need a (nice / nicely) cup of tea.

**5** I'm walking (slow / slowly) because I'm wearing new shoes.

**6** This photograph is not very (clear / clearly). Is that a dog or a cat?

**7** She spoke very (clear / clearly). I understood every word.

**8** That's a (good / well) idea.

**9** The rain is very (heavy / heavily). Let's stay at home.

**10** This question isn't (easy / easily).

**11** He spoke to her (nice / nicely).

**12** They studied hard for the exam and passed it (easy / easily).

**13** He's a good pianist. He plays (good / well).

**14** She was late, so she drove (quick / quickly).

**15** Those flowers are (beautiful / beautifully).

## 5 Make sentences

*Put the words in the right order to make sentences.*
**Examples:**
dangerously / he / drives
*He drives dangerously.*
this bus / dangerously / he is driving
*He is driving this bus dangerously.*

**1** the window / quietly / he closed

**2** the door / slowly / she opened

**3** the newspaper / she read / quickly

**4** they speak / well / English

**5** badly / sings / my uncle

**6** hard / they / work

**7** postcards / they / the / quickly / wrote

**8** she / beautifully / paints

**9** he ate / noisily / the biscuits

**10** they wash / very carefully / their new car

## Frequency Adverbs
### He never drinks coffee

## FORM

**1**   Look at these sentences.
*I am **often** late for work.*
*He **never** drinks coffee late at night.*
*Have you **always** lived in Canada?*
*Often, never* and *always* are frequency adverbs.
**2**   The most common frequency adverbs are
*always, never, normally, occasionally, often, rarely, sel-*
*dom, sometimes, usually* and *ever* (for negatives and
questions)

### POSITION OF FREQUENCY ADVERBS

**1**   After the verb *to be.*
**A**   In positive and negative sentences:
subject + *to be* + frequency adverb
*The train is **usually** full at this time of the day.*
*The train isn't **usually** full at this time of the day.*
**B**   In questions:

*to be* + subject + frequency adverb
***Is** the train **usually** full at this time of the day?*
**2**   After an auxiliary.
**A**   In positive and negative sentences:
subject + auxiliary + frequency adverb
*I've **always** lived in Scotland.*
*I haven't **always** lived in Scotland.*
**B**   In questions:
auxiliary + subject + frequency adverb
*Have you **always** lived in Scotland?*
**3**   Before a one-word verb.
**A**   In positive and negative sentences:
subject + (negative auxiliary) + frequency adverb +
one-word verb
*I **often eat** meat.*
*I **don't often eat** meat.*

## USE

Frequency adverbs tell you how often something happens. This list gives you an idea about how these
adverbs are used.
always .... 100%
usually .... 85%
normally .... 85%
often .... 70%
sometimes .... 50%

occasionally .... 35%
seldom .... 20%
rarely .... 20%
never .... 0%
*In the summer, I **never** have a bath – I **always** take a*
*shower. But in the winter, when it's very cold, I **some-***
***times** sit in a hot bath and read the newspaper.*
(Here, never = 0%, always = 100%, sometimes = 50%.)

### 1  Complete the sentences

*Complete the sentences by putting the adverb in*
*brackets in the correct position.*
**Example:**
He is late. (often)
*He is often late.*

1  I am late. (never)
2  The bus is early. (often)
3  My computer is wrong. (never)
4  It is cold here in winter. (usually)
5  The fruit in that supermarket is fresh. (always)
6  His room is untidy. (always)

### 2  Complete the sentences

*Complete the sentences by putting the adverb in*
*brackets in the correct position.*
**Example:**
I have been to Brazil. (never)
*I have never been to Brazil.*

1  You must hit my dog! (never)
2  He has played golf. (never)
3  I have eaten Indian food. (never)
4  He will love you. (always)
5  I have swum in the Atlantic. (often)
6  I have seen snow. (never)
7  You must tell a lie. (never)
8  You must tell the truth. (always)

## 3 Complete the sentences

*Complete the sentences by putting the adverb in brackets in the correct position.*
**Example:**
I sleep with the window open. (always)
*I always sleep with the window open.*

1 He plays the piano after lunch. (always)
2 I watch TV in the afternoon. (never)
3 I put sugar in my tea. (never)
4 I think about you. (often)
5 We start work at 8.30. (normally)
6 We have breakfast in the kitchen. (always)

## 4 Make questions

*Use the words to make present perfect questions. Put the adverb in brackets in the correct position.*
**Example:**
you / live / in Manchester? (always)
*Have you always lived in Manchester?*

1 he / work / in France? (ever)
2 they / be / to Singapore? (ever)
3 you / drive / German cars? (always)
4 you / build / a snowman? (ever)
5 she / live / in a house? (always)
6 they / eat / brown bread? (always)
7 you / fly / above a mountain? (ever)
8 you / be / to Africa? (ever)
9 she / be / to Asia? (ever)
10 you / have / short hair? (always)

## 5 Make questions

*Use the words to make present simple questions. Put the adverb in brackets in the correct position.*
**Examples:**
you / put / sugar in your tea? (always)
*Do you always put sugar in your tea?*
she / work / late? (sometimes)
*Does she sometimes work late?*

1 she / take / the same bus to work? (always)
2 you / see / Tom? (ever)
3 she / listen / to the radio in her car? (ever)
4 he / go / to the cinema? (ever)
5 you / tell / the truth? (always)
6 you / lie? (ever)
7 you / eat / biscuits in bed? (sometimes)
8 you / get up / at 7 o'clock? (normally)

9 he / go / to bed after midnight? (often)
10 you / drink / cold tea on a hot day? (ever)

## 6 Complete the story

*Complete the story by putting the frequency adverbs in the correct position. The first one has been done for you.*

My Aunt Beryl is different ...
1 She reads a book at breakfast. (always)
*She always reads a book at breakfast.*
2 She talks to anyone in the afternoon. (never)
3 She wears a hat in bed. (usually)
4 She sleeps in the garden. (sometimes)
5 She has used a telephone. (never)
6 She has eaten meat. (never)
7 She watches TV. (never)
8 In the winter she wears a T-shirt. (always)
9 In the summer she wears three jumpers and a coat. (usually)
10 She has lied to people. (never)
11 She has told the truth. (always)
12 She gives bird food to her cat and cat food to her bird. (usually)
13 She wears one red shoe and one blue shoe. (normally)
14 She has sung Italian songs on the bus. (often)
15 She gives money to people who live on the street. (always)
16 She is kind to me. (always)
17 She has forgotten my birthday! (never)
18 She gives me two presents – £100 and a potato. (usually)
19 I spend the money on her pets. (always)
20 I give bird food to her bird and cat food to her cat. (always)
21 Her pets are happy when it's my birthday. (always)

## USE

**ON**

**1**   With days
*on Monday, on Saturday, on Christmas Day, on New Year's Day*
*We'll see you **on** Tuesday.*
**Note:**
*On Wednesdays* means *every Wednesday*.
*I play tennis on Wednesdays.* (= *I play tennis every Wednesday.*)
**2**   With dates
*on 15th July, on 23rd October*
*I'm going to the dentist **on** 12th August.*

**IN**

**1**   For months
*in January, in December*
*My birthday is **in** July.*
**2**   For years
*in 1798, in 1983, in 1997*
*Guglielmo Marconi died **in** 1937.*
**3**   For seasons
*in the spring, in the summer, in the autumn, in the winter*
*I'm always happier **in** the spring.*
**4**   For periods of time
*in the 1970s (1970–1979), in the 20th century (1900–1999)*
*I was at school with her **in** the 1980s.*
**5**   For parts of the day
*in the morning, in the afternoon, in the evening* (general)

**Note:**
We say *at night* and *on Wednesday afternoon.* (specific)
**6**   To talk about the future
*I'll be there **in** an hour.*
*I'll be there **in** an hour's time.*
(It's 9.30 now. I'll be there at 10.30.)
*I'll see you **in** a couple of days.*
*I'll see you **in** a couple of days' time.*
(Today is Monday. I'll see you on Wednesday.)

**AT**

**1**   For times
*at 9.00, at 11.30, at midnight, at lunchtime, at dinner-time*
*The plane arrives **at** 10.15.*
**2**   For festivals
*at Easter, at Christmas*
**3**   For expressions like
*at the weekend, at the moment, at present, at once* (immediately)
***At** the moment, he's looking for a new job.*

**FROM ... TO**

To talk about the start and the finish of something, we use *from ... to.*
*The shop is open **from** 9 **to** 6.*
*They have lessons **from** Monday **to** Friday.*
In the same way, we say
*I'll be at the hotel **from** Monday.* (= Monday is the first day I am there.)

**Note:**
We do not use a preposition with *last, this* and *next*.
*I'll do it **this** week.* (not *I'll do it in this week.*)
*I saw her **last** year.*
*We'll be on holiday **next** month.*

---

### 1   Complete the sentences

*Complete the sentences with* at, in *or* on.

**1**   I'm going to Jamaica .......... Sunday.
**2**   I've got an important meeting .......... Thursday afternoon.
**3**   The bank is closed .......... Christmas Day.
**4**   We have lots of parties .......... Christmas.
**5**   The film starts .......... 8 o'clock. So, I'll pick you up .......... 7.30.
**6**   I'm busy .......... the moment. I'll call you back .......... a couple of minutes.
**7**   They got married .......... 1 o'clock .......... 12th November.
**8**   Will people live on the moon .......... the 21st century?
**9**   I was born .......... 29th March.
**10**   I met her .......... 1992.
**11**   Her birthday is .......... July
**12**   I prefer to go away .......... Easter.
**13**   He came here ....... Monday and he'll go back .......... a couple of weeks.
**14**   I don't like to go out ..... night.
**15**   The shops close ..... 6.30.

### 2   Complete the sentences

*Complete the sentences with* at, in *or* on.

**1**   She was born .......... 1982.

2 Are you free .......... the weekend.
3 He plays golf .......... Tuesdays.
4 I'm in a hurry. Do it .......... once!
5 I start university .......... three months' time.
6 He wants to be a film star but he's working in a hotel .......... present.
7 Can you come to lunch .......... Sunday?
8 These birds sleep .......... the winter and wake up .......... the spring.
9 I've got an appointment at the dentist's .......... 12.30 tomorrow.
10 They're going to a concert .......... 4th August.
11 In Sweden, it's still light .......... midnight .......... summer.
12 I'm sorry, I can't see him .......... the moment.
13 She'll be here .......... 3 o'clock.
14 Can I see you .......... lunchtime?
15 Tell him to wait, I'll talk to him .......... a minute.

### 3 Complete the sentences

*Complete the sentences with* at, in, on *or* from ... to.

1 I work in a restaurant .......... the afternoon.
2 I study .......... night.
3 The train will arrive .......... 1.30.
4 The plane will arrive .......... 20 minutes' time.
5 I'm living in Zurich .......... the moment.
6 The restaurant is open .......... 3 o'clock .......... the afternoon .......... 11 o'clock .......... night.
7 I work .......... Monday .......... Friday. But I'm free .......... the weekend.
8 I'm free .......... lunchtime. Shall we go and have a walk in the park?
9 The hotel is open .......... February .......... October. It's closed .......... the winter.
10 I've got an exam .......... 9 o'clock .......... Monday morning.
11 You're reading question 11 .......... the moment, but .......... a few seconds you'll read question 12.
12 The twins were born .......... 19th September. Tim was born .......... 11.32 .......... the morning and Jenny was born .......... 1.30 .......... the afternoon.
13 We're going on holiday next week. .......... a few days' time we'll be on a beach .......... 10.00 .......... 5.00 every day.
14 Long hair was very popular .......... the 1970s.
15 The school closes for a few weeks .......... Easter.
16 It's late. I'm going to bed. I'll see you ..........the morning.
17 The coach will arrive .......... 3.30 .......... Wednesday afternoon.

18 We're having a party .......... Thursday. Can you come?
19 I only work .......... Tuesday .......... Thursday.
20 She'll arrive in India .......... 4 'o clock in the morning.

### 4 Fill in the gaps

*Fill in the gaps in the story with prepositions of time.*

**(1)** .......... 1st January every year I decide to stop eating chocolate. But **(2)** .......... 2nd January I start again! I love chocolate. I eat it **(3)** .......... the morning, **(4)** .......... the afternoon, **(5)** .......... the evening and **(6)** .......... night! I eat it **(7)** .......... the spring, **(8)** .......... the summer, **(9)** .......... the autumn and **(10)** .......... the winter. I eat it **(11)** .......... lunchtime, **(12)** .......... teatime and **(13)** .......... dinnertime. I ate it in 1996, in 1997 ...

### 5 Choose the correct preposition

*Choose the correct prepostion in brackets and <u>underline</u> it.*

**Example:**
She'll be here (<u>at</u> / on) 11 o'clock.

1 I live in Spain (from / on) October (at / to) March.
2 Please do it (to / at) once.
3 Her birthday is (at / on) Christmas Day.
4 They always go away (at / in) Easter.
5 He always leaves work (from / at) 4 o' clock (in / on) Friday.
6 I'll do it (in / at) a moment.
7 Do you want to go to the cinema (from / on) Saturday?
8 Shall we go? (at / in) the afternoon or the evening?
9 I was on the beach (to / from) 9.00 in the morning (to / in) 5.00 in the evening.
10 I never go to work (in / at) the weekend.

## USE

### PREPOSITIONS OF PLACE

**1**   Look at the picture of the picnic below. These are some of the prepositions we use for places.

*The sandwiches are **on** a plate.*

*The orange juice is **in** a bottle.*

*There are some packets of crisps **in front of** the orange juice.*

*There is a cake **next to** some apples.*

*The picnic basket is **under** a tree.*

*Jolly, the dog, is **behind** the tree.*

*Joe Thompson is in the tree **above** the picnic basket.*

*Mr Thompson is sitting **opposite** his wife, Beryl. They are talking.*

*Sally Thompson is sitting **by** her father. She is eating an apple.*

*Their car is **near** the tree.*

**2**   These are some other ways to use prepositions of place.

**In**

**A**   to be in a city or country

*I live in Tokyo. Tokyo is in Japan.*

**B**   to be in the sky

*There are a lot of clouds in the sky today.*

**At**

**A**   to be at work, school, university

*Mary's at university in Manchester.*

**B**   to be at the doctor's or the dentist's

*Kevin's at the dentist's.*

**Note:**

We can also use a verb of movement + *by* with forms of transport,

*I came by bus, Uncle James came by car and Aunt Beryl arrived by taxi.*

but we always say *on foot*.

### PREPOSITIONS OF MOVEMENT

*Across, along, around, down, into, onto, out of, over, past, through, towards, up*

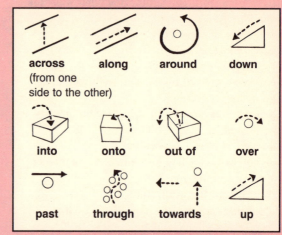

**across** (from one side to the other)    **along**    **around**    **down**

**into**    **onto**    **out of**    **over**

**past**    **through**    **towards**    **up**

*Carefully, Mrs Nunn walked **across** the busy road.*

*Please walk **along** the corridor! Don't run!*

*Paul and Jenny walked **around** the building, looking for a door.*

*We climbed slowly **up** the hill, than ran **down** the other side.*

*Helen put her key **into** her handbag then left the house.*

*The man with the long grey hair stepped **onto** a box and began to speak to us.*

*When she got home, Helen took her key **out of** her handbag and opened the door.*

*Young Harry climbed **over** the wall to get the football from Mr Wynn's garden.*

*I have to go **past** the post office on my way to work, so I'll post your letter for you.*

*James pushed his way **through** the crowd **towards** the theatre door, but he was too late – the actress was getting into a taxi.*

## 1　Choose the correct preposition

*Look at the picture. Then choose the correct preposition and underline it to answer the questions. The first one has been done for you.*

1　Where are the sandwiches?
　They are (under / <u>on</u>) the plate.
2　Where is the orange juice?
　It's (above / in) the bottle.
3　Where are the cakes?
　They're (next to / in) the apples.
4　Where are the crisps?
　They're (in front of / opposite) the orange juice.
5　Where is the picnic basket?
　It's (behind / under) the tree.
6　Where is the dog?
　It's (behind / under) the tree.
7　Where is the car?
　It's (near / on) the tree.
8　Where is Mr Thompson sitting?
　He's sitting (in front of / opposite) his wife.
9　Where is Joe Thompson?
　He's in the tree (under / above) the picnic basket.
10　Where is Sally sitting?
　She's sitting (on / by) her father.

## 2　Complete the sentences

*Complete the sentences with at, to, in or on.*
**Example:**
The Taj Mahal is *in* India.

1　Francesca's .......... the kitchen. She's making lunch.
2　The house is very quiet this afternoon. The children are .......... school.
3　Jim's got a cold. He's not .......... work today. He's .......... home in bed.
4　I was .......... the train for ten hours. I read my newspaper four times!
5　It was very hot .......... the coach. I fell asleep.
6　It's a long journey from Tokyo to Berlin. We were .......... the plane for 18 hours.
7　Can you meet me .......... the airport?
8　I saw Jackie .......... the bus. She was talking to Tina.
9　We're .......... holiday next week. We're going .......... Indonesia.
10　I bought these cakes .......... the baker's. Have one!
11　The smallest country .......... South America is Guyana.
　How do you know that?
　I read it .......... a book.

12　We are having a party .......... Jim's flat. Can you come?
13　I bought these oranges .......... the greengrocer's. They're wonderful!
14　Moscow is the biggest city .......... Russia.
15　I met Sally .......... the airport. She was .......... Kenya for a month. She sent you a postcard.
16　I met Tony .......... the doctor's. He was .......... bed with a cold for three days. He sent you his love.

## 3　Choose the correct preposition.

*James Promise is a film star. He is making a film in Hollywood about a man who loves danger. Unfortunately, James is a good actor but he doesn't like danger. So Fred is going to do the dangerous things. The director of the film is talking to Fred. Choose the correct preposition and underline it to complete the dialogue. The first one has been done for you.*

OK, Fred. You're going to be in the film. You're on a plane. The plane is flying (**1** <u>across</u> / under) Brazil.

This is the story. There's three kilos of gold on the plane. The gold is on the floor. You pick up the gold. You put it (**2** into / out of) your pocket.

Now, you're going to jump (**3** out of / up) the plane. You fall 300 metres (**4** into / across) the river.

There are dangerous fish in the river. OK, Fred? You swim (**5** into / across) the river and then get (**6** into / out of) the water.

There's grass near the river. It's two metres high. You run (**7** above / through) the grass and then you come (**8** up / to) a village. The people in the village hate you. They want the gold. They run towards you!

Then a helicopter flies 100 metres (**9** above / under) the village. You look (**10** down / up) at the helicopter.

There is a big man. He is looking (**11** into / out of) the window of the helicopter. He looks (**12** up / down) and sees you!

He hates you! He wants the gold! You run (**13** up / into) a hill and (**14** under / along) a road. The helicopter is flying (**15** on / above) your head! The man is angry. He is shouting at you! He takes a gun (**16** out of / into) his pocket and opens the door of the helicopter!

Then you see a lion! The lion is running (**17** towards / under) you. The people in the village are (**18** behind / under) you. The man in the helicopter is (**19** above / towards) your head. The lion is running towards you. Then ... Fred, Fred are you OK? You don't look very happy!

## USE

**AND**

We use *and* to join two events.

**1**   The subject of the events is the same

*She sat down **and** read the newspaper*.

In this case, *She sat down* is the first event; *She read the newspaper* is the second event.

**Note:**

When the subject of both verbs is the same, we do not need to repeat the subject.

**2**   The subject of the events is different

*The children sat down, **and** she read them a story*.

In this case, *The children sat down* is the first event; *she read them a story* is the second event.

**Note:**

When the subject of each verb is different, we put a comma before *and*.

**BUT**

We use *but* to connect events when we do not expect the second event.

**1**   The subject of the events is the same

*They ran to the station **but** missed the train*.

In this case, we expected them to catch the train.

**Note:**

When the subject of both verbs is the same, we do not need to repeat the subject.

**2**   The subject of the events is different

*Tom and Mary enjoy sport. Tom can swim, **but** Mary can't*.

**Notes:**

**1**   When the subject of each verb is different, we put a comma before *but*.

**2**   We do not repeat words that are the same for each part.

*Tom can swim, but Mary can't (swim)*.

The second use of *swim* is not necessary.

**AND or BUT**

We use *and* when we expect the second idea.

*He's very rich **and** lives in a big house*.

We use *but* when we do not expect the second idea.

*He's very rich **but** he lives in a very small house*.

---

**1**   **Complete the sentences**

*Complete the sentences with* and *or* but.

**Examples:**

I went to the shop *and* I bought a new dress.

I went to the shop *but* I didn't buy anything.

1   I bought a book .......... I didn't read it.
2   I bought an ice-cream .......... I ate it very slowly.
3   I bought a radio .......... I listen to it when I'm in the bath.
4   He was very tired .......... he fell asleep in front of the fire.
5   He was very tired .......... he went to the party and danced all night.
6   I'm a vegetarian .......... I never eat meat.
7   I like music .......... I can't play the piano.
8   I live in Tokyo .......... I can't speak Japanese.
9   I can speak Japanese .......... I've never been to Japan.
10   I love Italian food .......... I eat spaghetti every day.

**2**   **Join the ideas**

*Match the ideas in A and B, then join them with* and *or* but. *The first one has been done for you.*

| A | B |
|---|---|
| 1  It's the middle of winter | a)  he can lift 100 kg! |
| 2  I bought a wonderful camera | b)  combed it. |
| 3  She speaks Norwegian | c)  we're eating at three o'clock today. |
| 4  He doesn't look strong | d)  they wear expensive clothes. |
| 5  They're very poor | e)  he goes to the swimming pool every day. |
| 6  He loves swimming | f)  they have a lot of pets. |
| 7  We usually have lunch at midday | g)  she's never been to Norway. |
| 8  He washed his hair | h)  I take lots of photographs. |
| 9  They love animals | i)  it's very hot today. |

1   *It's the middle of winter but it's very hot today.*

## USE

### EITHER ... OR

We use *either ... or* when we are not certain which of two things is correct.

**1**    *either* + noun + *or* + noun

*Jenny is either **a teacher** or **a writer**.*

**2**    *either* + verb + *or* + verb

*I'm not sure what sport she does. She either **plays** tennis or she **swims**.*

**3**    *either* + sentence + *or* + sentence

*Either John married Mary or Stephen married her.*

We can also say:

*Either John or Stephen married Mary. I don't know which one.*

### NEITHER ... NOR

We use *neither ... nor* when we know that two ideas are wrong.

**1**    *neither* + noun + *nor* + noun

*Mary is neither **a dancer** nor **a singer**.*

**2**    *neither* + verb + *nor* + verb

*John neither **plays** tennis nor **swims**.*

**3**    When the verbs are the same but the subjects are different, then we usually say:

***Neither John nor Stephen** married Mary. I don't know who did.*

**Note:**

When there are two different subjects in a *neither ... nor* sentence, the verb is singular.

*Neither John nor Stephen **likes** fish.*

---

### 1   Complete the answers

*Complete the answers with* either ... or.

**Example:**

What's his favourite colour?

I can't remember. It's .......... (yellow / blue).

*I can't remember. It's either yellow or blue.*

1   What's her name?
    I'm not sure. It's .......... (Jackie / Jenny).
2   What does he do?
    I've forgotten. He's .......... (dentist / teacher).
3   What's for dinner?
    You decide. We can have .......... (fish / spaghetti).
4   When's her birthday?
    I'm not sure. It's .......... (Monday / Tuesday).
5   What is the capital of the USA?
    I'm not sure. It's .......... (Washington / New York).
6   Is the tomato a fruit?
    That's a good question! It's .......... (fruit / vegetable).
7   What's the most popular drink in the world?
    I don't know. It's .......... (tea / coffee).
8   How many days are there in February?
    That depends. There are .......... (28 / 29).
9   What time does the film start?
    I'm not sure. It's .......... (8.30 / 9.30).
10   When will you have your holiday?
    We haven't decided yet. It'll be .......... (June / July).

### 2   Join the sentences

*Join the sentences with* neither ... nor.

**Example:**

Jenny doesn't eat meat. Frank doesn't eat meat.

*Neither Jenny nor Frank eats meat.*

1   Jim can't swim. Vivienne can't swim.
2   My aunt can't speak Italian. My uncle can't speak Italian.
3   Carol doesn't like music. William doesn't like music.
4   Laura doesn't watch much television. Nicholas doesn't watch much television.
5   Ken doesn't drink tea. Theresa doesn't drink tea.
6   Tim doesn't work on Sundays. Tina doesn't work on Sundays.
7   Tony doesn't like chocolate. Sarah doesn't like chocolate.
8   Chris doesn't listen to the radio. Francesca doesn't listen to the radio.
9   Jenny can't type. Tom can't type.
10   Robert can't ride a bicycle. Patricia can't ride a bicycle.

# UNIT 41 Conjunctions 3: *so / because*

## USE

**1** Look at these sentences.
*I was thirsty **so** I drank some water.*
*I drank some water **because** I was thirsty.*
In these examples, *so* and *because* are conjunctions.
**2** We can say
*It was raining. I took my umbrella.*
Or we can join these sentences like this
a)  *I took my umbrella **because** it was raining.*
b)  *It was raining **so** I took my umbrella.*

Here, *so* means *and because of this* (*It was raining **and because of this** I took my umbrella*).
**3** In the above examples, the form is
a)  what + *because* + why  *I took my umbrella +*
                    *because + it was raining.*
b)  why + *so* + what  *It was raining + so + I took*
                    *my umbrella.*

---

### 1 Rewrite the sentences

*Rewrite the sentences using* so.
**Example:**
He cleaned the car because it was dirty.
*The car was dirty **so** he cleaned it.*

1  He changed his job because he wanted more money.
2  She worked hard because she wanted to pass her exams.
3  They swam in the river because they were very hot.
4  Jane ordered a large dinner because she was hungry.
5  I've seen that film five times because I like it very much.

### 2 Rewrite the sentences

*Rewrite the sentences using* because.
**Example:**
He wanted to please her so he bought her some flowers.
*He bought her some flowers **because** he wanted to please her.*

1  He needed more money so he got an evening job.
2  He loves chips so he often buys potatoes at the market.
3  She wanted to win the race so she trained every day.
4  The view was very beautiful so he took a photograph.
5  He was so very tall so he stood at the back of the group.

### 3 Complete the sentences

*Complete the sentences with* so *or* because.
**Example:**
I have 23 pets *so* I don't have any time for holidays.

1  I like films .......... I often go to the cinema.
2  I often go to the cinema .......... I like films.
3  It was very hot .......... I swam in the river.
4  I swam in the river .......... it was very hot.
5  We closed the window .......... it was cold.
6  It was cold .......... we closed the window.
7  They were thirsty .......... they drank some tea.
8  They drank some tea .......... they were thirsty.
9  He ate some fruit .......... he was hungry.
10 He was hungry .......... he ate some fruit.

### 4 Match and join

*Match the parts of the sentences. Then join them with* so *or* because. *The first one has been done for you.*
**Example:**
She was tired **so** she went to bed.

1  She was tired                a)  it tastes good.
2  They went to                 b)  she's passed her
   the grocer's                     exam.
3  The plates were dirty        c)  it was very cold.
4  The bus was late             d)  they had no butter.
5  It was raining this morning  e)  she went to bed.
6  I want to be a fisherman     f)  the grass is wet.
7  Tina is happy                g)  I love the sea.
8  They eat fast food           h)  they took a taxi.
9  I wore three jumpers         i)  I washed them.

82

*The questions in Revision Test 4 are about the grammar of Units 32–41. Choose the best answer, A, B or C.*

## UNITS 32-34

1   They bought three .... .
   A  expensive   B  expensive   C  expensives
      watch         watches        watches

2   She lives in a .... house.
   A  old,        B  new, nice   C  beautiful,
      beautiful                  old

3   Kelly is .... .
   A  as tall as   B  as Veronica   C  tall as
      Veronica       tall           Veronica

4   Tim .... as Tessa.
   A  not as    B  is not as rich   C  is not rich
      rich is

5   An apple is .... a potato.
   A  sweet than   B  sweeter as   C  sweeter than

6   Kenya is .... than Greenland.
   A  hoter      B  more hotter   C  hotter

7   The weather was bad yesterday. But today it's .... .
   A  badder    B  worse      C  worser

8   My aunt is .... woman in America.
   A  the richer   B  the most rich  C  the richest

9   What is the .... film you've ever seen?
   A  best       B  better     C  goodest

10  This is .... thing I've ever done.
   A  the more   B  the most    C  the
      dangerous    dangerous     dangerousest

## UNITS 35-36

11  It started to rain. They ran home .... .
   A  fastly     B  quickly    C  quickest

12  Does she .... ?
   A  sing well   B  well sing   C  sing good

13  He works .... .
   A  hardly    B  good      C  hard

14  He .... .
   A  the toast   B  ate the toast   C  quickly the
      quickly ate   quickly        toast ate

15  I have .... .
   A  never been   B  been to    C  been never
      to France    France never   to France

16  Have you .... ?
   A  in Canada   B  in always    C  always lived
      lived always  Canada lived   in Canada

17  Do you .... tennis at the weekend?
   A  play often   B  often playing  C  often play

18  .... to Asia?
   A  Have you   B  Been you   C  Ever been
      ever been    ever         you

19  She .... sugar in her tea.
   A  is never put  B  never puts   C  puts never

## UNITS 37-39

20  I'll see you .... Thursday.
   A  in         B  at         C  on

21  Those birds fly north .... the winter.
   A  in         B  at         C  on

22  I'm free .... lunchtime. Shall we have a walk in the park?
   A  in         B  at         C  on

23  The hotel is open .... February to September.
   A  from      B  of        C  at

24  We normally go to Scotland .... Easter.
   A  at         B  in         C  on

25  The orange juice is .... the bottle.
   A  in         B  of        C  at

26  Francesca's making lunch. She's .... the kitchen.
   A  at         B  with       C  in

27  Tokyo is .... Japan.
   A  at         B  on        C  in

28  What time does your plane arrive? I'll meet you .... the airport.
   A  at         B  on        C  to

29  We got .... at about 3.00 a.m.
   A  in home   B  at home    C  home

## UNITS 40-41

30  I can swim .... I can't dance.
   A  and       B  but       C  so

31  I can't remember her name. It's .... or Jane.
   A  Jenny either B  or Jenny    C  either Jenny

32  Neither John nor Tim .... speak Russian.
   A  can       B  can to     C  can't

33  He doesn't look very strong .... he can lift 100 kg.
   A  and       B  so       C  but

34  We were cold .... we put on our jumpers.
   A  so        B  because   C  but

35  We put on our jumpers .... we were so cold.
   A  because   B  it was    C  for why

*The questions in this test are about all 42 units in the book. The test will tell you if you are ready to go on to Penguin Grammar Workbook 2.*

## UNITS 1-5

1  She .... a dentist.
   A  are            B  is            C  am
2  .... very cold today.
   A  It's           B  Its           C  Weather
3  .... vegetables fresh?
   A  These are      B  Is this        C  Are these
4  She is very poor. She .... any money.
   A  doesn't have   B  haven't        C  don't have
5  .... a shower every day?
   A  Do you have    B  Has you got    C  Have you
                                          got
6  .... a post office near here?
   A  Are there      B  There are      C  Is there

## UNITS 6-10

7  He's a vegetarian. He .... meat.
   A  not eat        B  doesn't eat    C  doesn't eats
8  Mr Thompson .... mathematics at my school.
   A  teaches        B  teachs         C  teach
9  .... to Amsterdam?
   A  Do this        B  Does this      C  Does this
      train go           train go          train goes
10 When .... ?
   A  the film       B  the film       C  does the
      starts             starting          film start
11 Be quiet! The baby .... .
   A  sleeping       B  sleeps         C  is sleeping
12 What .... ?
   A  are you        B  you doing      C  do you
      doing                               doing
13 When .... tennis with Jane?
   A  is you         B  are you        C  you playing
      playing            playing
14 .... in a hotel at the moment?
   A  Do you stay    B  Are you        C  Does you
                        staying            stay
15 I .... cold weather.
   A  hates          B  hate           C  am hating
16 I .... to work by train.
   A  am going       B  go normally    C  normally go
      normally
17 The French word 'bonjour' .... 'hello'.
   A  means          B  is meaning     C  mean

## UNITS 11-15

18 .... that!
   A  Don't to do    B  Don't doing    C  Don't do
19 When .... in Portugal?
   A  you were       B  were you       C  was you
20 It .... a lot yesterday.
   A  has rained     B  raining        C  rained
21 Mr Rolls and Mr Royce .... their first car in 1906.
   A  built          B  builded        C  build
22 Did .... the homework last night?
   A  you do         B  you did        C  do you
23 They .... television when you rang.
   A  watching       B  were           C  watched
                        watching

## UNITS 16-21

24 Francesca's not here. She .... to the bank.
   A  has went       B  gone           C  has gone
25 My hair is wet. I've .... washed it.
   A  yet            B  just           C  going to
26 Have you ever .... to Hong Kong?
   A  been           B  be             C  go
27 We're going to buy a new house .... .
   A  yesterday      B  in 1994        C  next year
28 The train .... at 11.30.
   A  is going       B  arriving       C  will arrive
      arrive
29 You .... in the classroom. Take your sandwiches outside.
   A  must to eat    B  mustn't eat    C  mustn't
                                          to eat
30 You .... pay to use the library. It's free.
   A  don't          B  don't have     C  mustn't
      have to
31 Please speak slowly. I .... English very well.
   A  can't          B  can't to       C  can't
      understand        understand        under–
                                          standing

## UNITS 22-23

32 .... sisters do you have?
   A  How much       B  How many       C  Many
33 .... jumper did you wear – the yellow one or the green one?
   A  How            B  Who            C  Which
34 'Who .... to Tim?' 'Mary.'
   A  did Mary       B  did write      C  wrote
      write

## UNITS 24-31

35 Madrid is .... city.

A an European    B a European    C European

36 She lives .... West Indies.

A in the          B in a          C in

37 Can you see .... green house on the hill? I live there.

A these          B those         C that

38 My uncle is very rich. .... has five houses!

A He          B Him         C His

39 My sister lives in Australia. I phoned .... yesterday.

A she          B hers         C her

40 Is this pen mine or .... ?

A you          B your         C yours

41 .... bicycle is red.

A Francesca's    B Francesca    C Of Francesca

42 The .... beautiful today.

A weather is      B weather      C weather are

43 Is there a petrol station near here? We don't have .... petrol in the car.

A some          B many         C much

44 I'm making some sandwiches for the party. I bought three .... of bread.

A loaf          B loafs         C loaves

## UNITS 32-41

45 Fred wears .... shoes.

A plastic, old brown    B brown, plastic old    C old, brown plastic

46 Jenny is not .... Jane.

A as tall like    B as tall as    C tall as

47 This is the .... film I've ever seen.

A best          B better         C goodest

48 They .... .

A beautifully sing    B sing beautifully    C sing beautiful

49 We .... to Brazil

A been never have    B never have been    C have never been

50 You did well in the test .... you can now do *Book 2*.

A because      B so      C either

# Glossary of Terms

**Clause** – a clause is a sentence or part of a sentence. It must have a subject and a finite verb.

*The man sat on the bridge.* (one clause = one sentence).

*When I saw him, he was crossing the street.*(two clauses = one sentence)

**Noun** – nouns refer to people (*man, girl*), animals (*cat, lion*), birds (*eagle, owl*), places (*valley, town, village*) or things (*table, ball*). You can count some nouns (*table, dog*), but there are some nouns you can't count (*coffee, furniture, information*).

**Object** – the noun or pronoun which comes after the verb in the clause or sentence.

*John climbed the tree.* (Here *the tree* is the object.)

*Peter met her in the high street* (Here, *her* is the object.)

**Preposition** – a word followed by a noun or pronoun which tells you the position of something or refers to a time.

*On the table* (position)

*On Wednesday* (time)

**Pronoun** – a word that replaces a noun.

*The man was standing on the corner. John saw him.* (Here *him* replaces *the man*.)

*Peter met Mary after work. Then they went for a walk.* (Here *they* replaces *Peter* and *Mary*.)

**Sentence** – this is the largest grammatical unit. Most sentences are just one clause, but there can be many clauses in a sentence. It begins with a capital letter and ends with a full stop.

**Subject** – the noun or pronoun in the clause or sentence which comes before the verb. There is a subject in every clause or sentence.

*The woman left home early.* (Here *the woman* is the subject.)

*Rita bought a new dress.* (Here *Rita* is the subject.)

**Syllable** – this is a part of a word which has one vowel sound. Words can have several syllables.

*Car* has one syllable.

*Mo–ney* has two syllables.

*Beau–ti–ful* has three syllables.

**Verb** – a word which refers to events or situations or conditions: *make, do, run, feel, think*

    **Auxiliary verb** – a verb which helps the main verb For questions or negative statements, we often use *do* as an auxiliary.

    *Do you work every day?*

    *We **didn't** see him last week.*

    In the present perfect, we use *have* as an auxiliary.

    *Mary **has** gone to school.*

    There are also **modal auxiliaries** such as *must, can, may*. We always put a main verb after an auxiliary verb.

    **Finite verb:** this part of the verb shows the tense – present or past

    *arrive – arrived*

    There must be a finite verb in every clause or sentence.

    **Infinitive:** this is the base verb with *to*.

    *to make, to arrive to come*

**Vowel** – there are five letters in English which help to make vowel sounds – *a, e, i, o, u.*

85

# Irregular Verbs

| PRESENT SIMPLE/ INFINITIVE | PAST SIMPLE | PAST PARTICIPLE | PRESENT SIMPLE/ INFINITIVE | PAST SIMPLE | PAST PARTICIPLE |
|---|---|---|---|---|---|
| be | was / were | been | leave | left | left |
| become | became | become | lend | lent | lent |
| begin | began | begun | let | let | let |
| bite | bit | bitten | lie | lay | lain |
| blow | blew | blown | light | lit | lit |
| break | broke | broken | lose | lost | lost |
| bring | brought | brought | make | made | made |
| build | built | built | meet | met | met |
| buy | bought | bought | pay | paid | paid |
| catch | caught | caught | put | put | put |
| choose | chose | chosen | read | read | read |
| come | came | come | ride | rode | ridden |
| cut | cut | cut | ring | rang | rung |
| dig | dug | dug | run | ran | run |
| do | did | done | say | said | said |
| draw | drew | drawn | see | saw | seen |
| drink | drank | drunk | sell | sold | sold |
| drive | drove | driven | send | sent | sent |
| eat | ate | eaten | shine | shone | shone |
| fall | fell | fallen | show | showed | shown |
| feed | fed | fed | shut | shut | shut |
| fight | fought | fought | sing | sang | sung |
| find | found | found | sit | sat | sat |
| fly | flew | flown | sleep | slept | slept |
| forget | forgot | forgotten | speak | spoke | spoken |
| forgive | forgave | forgiven | spend | spent | spent |
| get | got | got | stand | stood | stood |
| give | gave | given | steal | stole | stolen |
| go | went | gone | swim | swam | swum |
| grow | grew | grown | take | took | taken |
| hang | hung | hung | teach | taught | taught |
| have | had | had | tell | told | told |
| hear | heard | heard | think | thought | thought |
| hit | hit | hit | throw | threw | thrown |
| hold | held | held | understand | understood | understood |
| hurt | hurt | hurt | wake | woke | woken |
| keep | kept | kept | wear | wore | worn |
| know | knew | known | win | won | won |
| lay | laid | laid | write | wrote | written |
| lead | led | led | | | |

# Punctuation and Spelling

## Punctuation
### CAPITAL LETTERS
We use capital letters for

1    the word at the beginning of a sentence:
*The day started well for John.*
*It was the best time of the year.*

2    whenever we use the first person singular *I*:
*I met him in the evening.*
*You and I must go to the theatre together soon.*

3    with names of people and places, titles of books and journals, days of the week and months:
*Gillian Wright*
*War and Peace*
*Mount Everest*
*The Times*
*Tuesday*
*June*

### FULL STOP
We put a full stop at the end

1    of sentences which are statements:
*It rained all night.*

2    or imperative forms which are not strong orders:
*Come home early.*

### COMMA
We use a comma when

1    we are connecting two main clauses with *and* or *but*, if the subject is different in each clause:
*He left home and went to work.*
(No comma – the subject is the same in each clause.)
*She left home early, but the train was very late.*
(Comma – the subject is different in each clause.

2    after a subordinate clause:
*When he came home, he felt very angry.*

3    but not before a subordinate clause
*He felt very angry when he came home.*

4    after an adverbial or prepositional phrase:
*On Sunday, I'll meet Anne.*

5    but not before an adverbial or prepositional phrase:
*I'll meet Anne on Sunday.*

## Spelling
### PLURAL NOUNS
#### Regular forms

1    Most nouns add *s* to the singular when they become plural.
*book – books, apple – apples*

2    For nouns ending in *ch, sh, s, ss, x* in the singular, add *es* to the noun to make the plural form.
*watch – watches, wish – wishes, bus – buses, box – boxes*

3    For nouns ending in consonant + *y* in the singular, change *y* to *i* and add *es* to make the plural form.
*baby – babies, lady – ladies*

4    For nouns ending in vowel + *y* in the singular, add only *s* to make the plural form.
*day – days, monkey – monkeys*

#### Irregular forms

1    For some nouns that end in *o* add *es* to form the plural.
*potato – potatoes, tomato – tomatoes, hero – heroes*

2    For some nouns that end in *f* or *fe*, change the *f* to *v* and add *es*.
*calf – calves, half – halves, wife – wives*

3    There are six important nouns which change completely.
*foot – feet, tooth – teeth, man – men, woman – women, mouse – mice, child – children*

4    Some nouns do not have a different form for the plural.
*sheep – sheep, deer – deer, aircraft – aircraft*

### DOUBLING CONSONANTS
#### Words with one syllable
Verbs and adjectives that end in vowel + consonant (e.g. *to stop, to plan, wet, thin*) double the consonant before adding an ending.
For verbs *-ed* or *-ing*:
*stop – stopped – stopping*
*plan – planned – planning*
*rub – rubbed – rubbing*
For adjectives *-er* or *-est*:
*wet – wetter – wettest*
*thin – thinner – thinnest*
*big – bigger – biggest*

#### Words with more than one syllable

1    For verbs that end in vowel + consonant (e.g. *prefer, begin, visit*) we double the consonant when the final syllable is stressed.
*prefer – preferred –  preferring*
*begin –              beginning* (*begin* is an irregular verb in the past)
*permit – permitted – permitting*
*regret – regretted –  regretting*

2    When the final syllable is not stressed, we do not double the final consonant.
*visit – visited – visiting*
*remember – remembered – remembering*
*happen – happened – happening*

3    In British English, for verbs ending in *l*, put *ll* before -*ed* or -*ing*.
*travel – travelled – travelling*

**Note:**
In American English they do not double the *l*.
travel – traveled – traveling